PRAISE FOR RO~~BERT OLEN BUTLER~~

A Good Scent from a Strange Mountain

'The book has attracted such acclaim not simply because
it is beautifully and powerfully written, but because it convincingly
pulls off an immense imaginative risk... Butler has not only entered
the significant and ever-growing canon of Vietnam-related fiction
(he has long been a member) he has changed its composition forever'
– Claire Messud, *Guardian*

'Deeply affecting ... a brilliant collection of stories about
storytellers whose recited folklore radiates as implicit prayer ...
One of the strongest collections I've read in ages'
– Ann Beattie

'*A Good Scent From a Strange Mountain* is remarkable...
for how beautifully it achieves its daring project
of making the Vietnamese real'
– *New York Times Book Review*

'Butler's achievement is not only to reveal the inner lives of
the Vietnamese, but to show, through their eyes, how the rest
of us appear from an outside perspective'
– *Chicago Tribune*

A Small Hotel

'With mesmerizing detail, Butler excavates layers of memory
and illuminates moments of both tenderness and alienation'
– New Yorker

'Skillful... Absorbing... Wise and painfully realistic...
A novel of ideas, an interrogation of the limitations and uses of language'
– New York Times Book Review

'Intelligent, deeply moving... remarkably written...
A Small Hotel is a masterful story that will remind readers
once again why Robert Olen Butler has been called
the best living American writer'
– Fort Worth Star Telegram

'A sleek, erotic, and suspenseful drama about men
who cannot say the word love and the women they harm...
Butler executes a plot twist of profound proportions in this
gorgeously controlled, unnerving, and beautifully revealing
tale of the consequences of emotional withholding'
– Booklist (starred review)

'A brief, intense portrayal of the collapse of a marriage... This may be
the oldest story in the world, or at least in the monogamous world,
but Butler... seeks to give it new life by anatomizing the feelings
and perceptions of each of the principals... in *A Small Hotel* he has
performed an unusual and worthy feat. The puzzle may have only
three pieces, but each of these has many facets, and the way
they eventually fit together delivers a surprising charge'
– Washington Post

Christopher Marlowe 'Kit' Cobb series

'a genuine and exhilarating success'
— Times Literary Supplement

'An exciting story... *The Hot Country* is a thinking person's
thriller, the kind of exotic adventure that, in better days,
would have been filmed by Sam Peckinpah'
— Washington Post

'a historical thriller of admirable depth and intelligence'
— BBC History Magazine

'high-spirited adventure... great writing'
— New York Times

'one hell of a read... an exhilarating and enjoyable read
with plenty of drama and a very likeable leading man...
I guarantee you will be eagerly awaiting the next
instalment in this new series'
— We Love This Book

'Literate, funny, action-packed, vivid, and intriguing'
— Historical Novel Society

'A fine stylist, Butler renders the time and place in perfect detail'
— Publishers Weekly

'the novel is not only shot through with keen intelligence
but couched in elegant prose'
— crimetime.co.uk

ALSO BY ROBERT OLEN BUTLER

* Published by No Exit Press

Severance

Severance

STORIES

ROBERT OLEN BUTLER

NOEXIT2

First published in the UK in 2016
by No Exit Press, an imprint of Oldcastle Books
PO Box 394,
Harpenden, AL5 1XJ, UK

noexit.co.uk
@noexitpress

The stories in this book originally appeared in *Agni Magazine, The Cincinnati
Review, Five Points, The Georgia Review, Glimmer Train, The Kenyon Review,
McSweeney's, Ninth Letter, Open City, Prairie Schooner, The Southern Review,
Tin House, 21 Magazine, The Virginia Quarterly Review,* and *Water-Stone Review.*

ISBN
978-1-84344-759-7 (print)
978–1–84344–756-6 (epub)
978-1-84344-757-3 (kindle)
978-1-84344-758-0 (pdf)

2 4 6 8 10 9 7 5 3 1

Design and Typesetting by Elsa Mathern
Printed and bound in Great Britain by Clays Ltd, St Ives plc

For news, events and FREE stuff sign up at noexit.co.uk/news

The Heads

With special thanks to Jay Schaefer, Catherine Argand, and Isabelle Reinharez, and to David Baker, James Cummins, and David Lehman.

After careful study and due deliberation it is my opinion the head remains conscious for one minute and a half after decapitation.

– DR DASSY D'ESTAING, 1883

In a heightened state of emotion, we speak at the rate of 160 words per minute.

– DR EMILY REASONER, *A Sourcebook of Speech*, 1975

FOR ELIZABETH

This book began when I showed you my beloved Saigon
and we stood before the guillotine at the War Crimes
Museum, long before the fall of the blade.

MUD
Man

Beheaded by saber-toothed tiger

CIRCA 40,000 B.C.

sharp the air with cold that comes so fast, and far we all run, along water turning to rock, many suns and only short-snout and short-snout to eat between us, the old of us lagging, the cold rushing, the touchwood barely warm we blow long on the touchwood last darktime, we blow and much growling anger for the touchwood keeps its flame tight, we all will lose the flame soon, and we alone fall back to the old ones in skins but we all keep the body-grease for our ourselves to hold our heat inside while the old carry the cold inside, and one is the suckle woman, long suns past she holds us alone to her suckle and we alone sit at flame and suckle woman puts her hand upon our head alone and puts her mouth to our ear alone and makes a soft cry, but we all feel the time coming like many suns past, before suckle woman is old, and there were other old and the cold came quick and we all were drawn tight on our bones and the biting was fierce in our centers and we all were going slow and it was time to eat, to eat the old, and now the cold is upon us and now the time is again and we alone fall back to hold the suckle woman and to make cries into her ear before we all eat

MEDUSA

Gorgon and former human beauty

Beheaded by Perseus

CIRCA 2000 B.C.

dreaming, surely I dream now: I can still shake my hair down long and billowing like waves upon the sea, how tender I am how fair I can see in the reflection of water and shield and a man's eyes, and this softer hair makes no difference I still turn a man to stone who looks at me, the part of him that snakes inside me, a clefting of stone, and my body weeps the sea, pours forth the thickest sea for my god-man Poseidon who smells of brine and the great swimming creatures who attend him scaled and heavy wet limbs about me and that bitch Athena thinks her temple defiled but it was he who came to me and leaned his trident upon her marble face and dripped upon her floor, she tries to hurt me but I love my living hair these serpents whisper when men come close each strand with a split tongue hissing my desire for them I shake my dear children my tresses down and they curl back up their black eyes flashing and the man cries out at my beauty and then his tongue and face and chest and arms and thighs and his toad-headed serpent all turn hard forever the clearing before my cave is thronged with them my admirers, but my children are my true loves rooted in my brain and gathered sleeping against my face muttering sibilant dreams of love

MARCUS TULLIUS **CICERO**

Orator and politician

Beheaded on orders of Marc Antony

43 B.C.

louder, Marcus Tullius, I cannot hear you cries Helvia my noble mother her forehead ringed in curls calling from the top row of the empty theater *speak louder* and my arms are leaden from a thousand apt gestures and I cannot think and I am small *stand straight* she cries I lift my upper body and the senators are packed before me like sardelles straight from the sea their eyes unblinking their mouths gaping my voice rings through the curia and I feel the comforting press of my toga over my shoulder and now the senate is empty but for Antony *speak up* he says *I cannot hear you* his centurions are nowhere in sight and I straighten and say *if, noble Antony, your nobility were made coinage for the empire its measure would be* – I falter – I adjust the toga folds about my chest, searching for an appropriately minuscule measure – but time is running quickly, I know – I have no arms to lift – *your nobility* I say *is the nobility of green flies on goat shit they glitter in the sunlight and they eat and they move their wings and fly but their life is short* and Antony lifts up on diaphanous wings and rises and vanishes and now a woman's voice says *speak up, Marcus Tullius, speak up I cannot hear you* and I say *o noble mother, Helvia, if your nobility were made coinage for the empire*

21

JOHN THE BAPTIST
Prophet

Beheaded by King Herod

CIRCA 30

smelling of garlic he comes to me and he is lank with long hands and I rejoice that he enjoys his food and that in my own mouth there was only the bitter crunch of locust and the sour berry and the cloying of wild honey as I waited for him and I draw my face close to his mouth as I hold him in my arms to smell his very breath and I feel the hardness of his back and his hand curls up to cup my elbow angled by his side I pull that arm closer laying it along his body feeling his ribs and the Jordan rushes about us the fish rubbing at my legs like hungry dogs and I am hungry too and I would rub against him, my Lord my face of God, his eyes dark and narrowing at me as I hesitate to press him under and he whispers to me *John you must do this* and my mouth would speak but it is so close to his now and I lift him slightly toward me this man I have waited for all my life, waited to kiss, thinking it would be his feet but now I would have him open his mouth and devour me take me in his mouth and let me disappear into his very flesh and I would be sweet to his taste I am certain and he says *John*

VALERIA **MESSALINA**

Wife of Emperor Claudius I of Rome

Beheaded by order of her husband

48

I am sighted through my tongue I run the tip of my tongue through the cleft of his chin watching him and I hear through my tongue I draw my tongue across his chest and pause and listen to his heart beating, rushing faster even as I linger here, and I lift my face from the chest of my Caius Silius we are panting now we are the Circus Maximus we are the rush of wheels the wild breath of horses on the throne room floor the bright expanse of marble I shift my eyes and I see us both in the mirror of stone our flanks naked and pressed together as one I return my eyes to him, his head reclines, he sighs, I memorize his flesh the faint groove along the underside of his jaw the marble expanse of his chest this cinnamon nipple I pluck now with my lips and just below it is the red birth spot, the kiss of the goddess Voluptas: I have turned my eyes away from this too long, I will pull down her temple for this, I draw a circle around this spot on his flesh with my tongue I take it between my teeth tugging gently and he moans and I bite hard now his skin yielding his blood sudden and warm his body thrashes but I hold fast to my man I tear this other kiss from his body

DIOSCORUS
Shipmaster and companion to Paul

Beheaded by Roman soldiers who mistook him for the apostle

67

sails swell and braces hum overhead, my hand on the tiller night and day and night again and all the things of the world are beneath my feet now, all at once, the timber and the cattle and the linen and the glass, the wine, the wool, ivory and apes, olives and cheese, plums and pears and pomegranates and ginger, myrrh and incense, alabaster and amber, oysters and slaves, their dark eyes turning to me awake in the midst of the night as I hug the coast out of Aden and it's day now and still I have wind in the great middle sea and I have woodwork and statuary from Sicily and papyrus and granite and glass from Egypt, corn and fish and hides from the Black Sea and from Smyrna I have carpets rolled and bound and stacked in the hold, and passengers, a man and two others who bow to him a man with a naked head like mine bare to the sky and the wind, there is only the terrible motionlessness of my house, becalmed, my son barely drawing a breath, this man touches my son's head and speaks to his god and my son lives and the man says *leave all these things* and I am in a marketplace and I cry out the name of this man's god as if into a gale and around me are figs and linen and vessels of clay

PAUL
(SAUL OF TARSUS)
Apostle

Beheaded by the Emperor Nero

67

narrow the gate through to the warren of merchants past figs and linen and clay vessels the smells of wood fire and bodies moving in the shadows of houses I am restless in my limbs and the way turns to a square a fountain and a great and sudden flare of light, I close my eyes to the welter of it blinded and open them again, and in the center of this brilliance a woman young her hair loose radiant her forearms bare she is bent to draw water and she lifts her face to me her eyes dark in the midst of the light which roils silently all about her and within me and I would move to her now and kneel before the mysteries of her body I am tumescent with devotion but instantly she turns her face away and I hesitate gasping waiting, if she but speak if she but call me to her, for all my readiness to act I wait and my horse nickers at my restlessness the land flat to the horizons my body sucked dry by the sun Damascus ahead and heretic Jews to shackle at the wrists at the ankles and the air around me ignites I am at the center of a flame and I am tumbling down I am on my knees I lift my face to see her and instead I hear a voice, a man, and I understand

MATTHEW
Tax collector and apostle

Beheaded by King Hirtacus of Ethiopia

78

faintly bitter, the smell of this wine, the old man stands with eyes rheumy in the shade of my custom shack and he says *please honorable publican this is very low quality wine* and I say *it is wormwood wine which adds twenty-five percent to the value at thirteen percent tax you owe the Empire three drachmas for these goods* and I wait for him to appeal my application of the highest allowed duty and then I will explain the further tax on horse and cart and wheels and the bridge he must cross and I will listen and allow him to convince me to lower the rate of duty by a few points and this will still leave me ample profit my thumb sliding up and down my forefinger on my writing hand I wait and he is silent and beyond him the Sea of Galilee is bright from the sun but it is more than that, the tips of the upchurning waves are flames rising and I begin to tremble and now a day of clouds and a fine misty rain and he says *follow me* and we are at Cana, he and the others he's called and his mother, and there is no wine and he passes his hand over six jugs of water and I sniff there and it is fine aged wine at ten drachmas per jug at thirteen percent duty *be still* he says

VALENTINE
Roman priest and saint

Beheaded by Emperor Claudius II

CIRCA 270

in she pads and crouches over me, quietly, the she-wolf, I am in her cave, not beneath the fig tree where Romulus and Remus cry in hunger, she has abandoned them to give me her tit and the cave is my jail cell and I wake ready to die for my Lord, His name on my lips, the dream a dream from my childhood before Christ and I crouch tiny in our doorway and naked men run by striking the backs of women who willingly bare their flesh to receive the lash of goatskin, receiving fertility on the day of Lupercalia, and Julia appears now at my cell door, daughter of Asterius my jailer, her eyes sightless from birth, I rise and cross to her and take the cup of water and the crust of bread and I drop them at once, knowing this time my hands are filled with the Spirit and I need only touch her eyelids and she will see, and her hair falls soft about her shoulders and I hesitate, my loins filling, and in my head the sound of naked men rushing past and we bare our backs, we priests, ready for the lash of God, and her face is lambent, turned slightly aside, and I slough off my clothes: I am naked, visibly filled with the ache of men, and I lay my thumbs lightly on her eyes so she can see her Valentine

DRAGON

Beast

Beheaded by Saint George

301

fly and land and run upon the pale fleshy jitteries I breathe hot upon them
their wailing comes then and in my mouth the soft flail of their limbs the
pulpy oozy of them and the cracky breaking, this body I eat nice body, oozy
too this blood I drink nice blood, I settle my legs and I fold my wings the
quieting comes upon me now after the bodies and the blood, all the rushy
sputtery in my center is gone, the flying and landing and running all done,
more of the fleshies dashing off I watch them and they seem now much like
my eggy littles come forth, my wings are still, I close my eyes and open them
and all around are the quivery greentops and the great ball of breath above,
I will fly up that high sometime but now I am in a peaceful dawdle that I
don't understand, full in the center and sweet heavy in my legs and fluttery
of the wingtips, and I lick the air and again and one of these I eat is before
me just a dashy-run across the way I ask my center if it wants this bit more
and I rise and I rush and this one looks not soft but glinty all over him with
the light and he sits on a long-face creature and he makes a sign at me up
and down and across

GEORGE
Soldier and saint

Beheaded by the Emperor Diocletian

303

far across the field the evil thing sits, small-seeming from here, my horse rears and frets sensing the ancient beast as all creatures of God do, while in my ears I still hear the voices of the villagers *a dragon* they cry, and so it is, I see the evil one as I have never seen him before, complacent in a meadow beneath the sun his scaled body the color of a toad his breath a faint hiss in the air wisps of smoke rising like morning mist about him the villagers cry *my daughter eaten my son eaten my husband* and I tell them of the Lord God and his own son whose body also was destroyed and they cry *that did us no good* and they wail on and I say *it did you no good because you have not eaten of your savior* and I kneel before a priest in a secret place in Rome and I eat the body and the blood and afterwards I say *father shall I leave my arms* and he says *fight in the Lord's name* and now I sit on the edge of this ignorant village and the dragon lifts his head and unfurls his wings and I thump my fist upon my breastplate and I draw my sword and in the center of me there is only the peace that passes all understanding because of the things I have eaten

THE LADY OF THE LAKE
Enchantress

Beheaded by Balin, the Knight of the Two Swords

CIRCA 470

diving deep I swim in his beard my breath giving out quickly in spite of all I know to do, all that he has taught me, my Merlin, he has schooled me in the things of the pot – the dragon's blood and the mistletoe and the black willow – he has yoked my dreams to my will, he has fed me four poisons – mandrake and henbane and nightshade and his blunt-headed sword, his manthing – he has fed me these till I was safe from each till my skin no longer crawled and my muscles no longer seized and my bones no longer quaked and instead I became strong and cunning and master of the elements and he has shown me how to bare my breasts and my loins and dance silently and I dance while he sleeps and I spin and cry out and he falls deeper into sleep and his staff rolls off his fingertips and I lift his cloak and he must be dreaming of me for his sword is raised and I put my hand to it and pluck it off – he will enter no other lady now he will live out his life with the memory of me – and it grows in my hand and hardens into steel and its torn root heals into hilt and pommel and I dive deep into my black water where I will wait his summons and I call his sword Excalibur

AH BALAM

Mayan ballplayer

Beheaded by custom as captain of losing team

803

life is held within the ball the lives of all the world's people and the sky is over us and the high walls are about us with the stone circle the gateway to heaven fixed there far above and the sun has swung from low to high as we play for the king and for our fate for the year to come, the skull of Ah Pitzlaw the Great is inside the rubber globe so it flies higher today the ring score is possible, weary I plant my foot and leap and hit the ball with my hip Ah Mun my brother sliding alongside and forward to take the next volley of the team of Ah Peku his small striker catching my volley on the knee and it flies up I am descended upon my two feet and squaring forward the ball lifting over my head and Ah Tabai behind me cries like the macaw and the ball slips low from him past my shoulder and caroms from the right wall and Ah Peku himself is running already for a mighty hip shot and I see our ancestors the first men on earth playing ball with the Lords of Death and even as Ah Peku flies toward the hanging ball I know I will end headless like the first men, my hands, useless in this game, tremble, but my heart is ready, the ball flies up and through the circle

PIERS **GAVESTON**

Male consort to King Edward II

Beheaded by posse of English nobles

1312

Edward's gift at my throat my head pushed down rough and I touch my emerald brooch my king gives me emerald and sapphire and ruby we are bright color, he and I, we are fields and sky and pomegranates his mouth smeared with the ruby juice sweet and sharp and I carry his crown soft on a pillow woven of gold, his child-wife put aside for his Piers for his sweet man she watches his crowning like a cameo face of milky glass pinned against a vast cloak of a crowd and I am draped in purple velvet bestarred with pearls the barons also watching us, my Edward and me, they are drops of piss in the king's great sea they push my head roughly down and I touch my emerald hidden in my clothes holding my silken self together my secret smooth stone en cabochon polished round as the tip of the Green Man's member as green as the deep forest, my king and I riding, the heat of my horse the chuff of its breath we are in flight and I am happy my sweet Ed my sweet Ned my sweet Eddy and we run from all the others and night comes and we unbuckle we unbrooch we unburden he says my name and I say his and it is dark and now we are alone in the world we are polished stones we are orbs and scepters

GOOSENECK
(GANSNACKEN)
Court jester to Duke Eberhard the Bearded

Beheaded by his master

1494

quickly, my lord arrives soon, I tether the goat and place the crest of my lord's defeated enemy round its neck and put my oft-merrily-used floppy crown on my ass-eared hat its bells jingling as if in laughter already at my jest and I have secured the rope in the ceiling beam and I stretch and draw myself up, hanging for a moment, breathless from my own wit, my father places his hand on my shoulder and pushes me toward the Duke descended from his horse and laughing at the belt of choked geese around my waist, me wishing to keep their feet dry I say, and he laughs loud and I am excited by this sound, my jokes are my lovers thrilling me, and he takes me to Württemberg and a life of mirth and he will soon be here I begin to swing on the rope, pulling hard at it and I am swinging faster and the goat looks up at me and I wave at him whom I will, as the great Duke, shortly leap upon in antic triumph and the door opens and it is the Duke and I am a jester not a sailor the goat breaks his knot and bolts just as I leap from the rope and fly at my stricken lord and fall heavy upon him, crotch to face, and alas I am already full excited at my joke, like a lover

THOMAS **MORE**
Lord Chancellor of England and saint

Beheaded by King Henry VIII for opposing his divorce

1535

arm around my neck the king leads me out among my roses the Thames
sliding heavily along just beyond the rosemary hedge *you never fail me*
he says, tugging me closer in the crook of his arm his breath on my face
smelling of pheasant and ale from my table *let's speak now of the stars
spinning round the earth* he says, and I sit in a palace hall the king and
Catherine the queen beside him and the plates are of gold and the servants
are backtreading softly and there is not a sound, we wait for Henry's hands
to open from the fists beside his plate and the peacocks are before us their
bright plumes vanished their flesh darkened by the fire and waiting, the king
loosens his right hand and takes up a knife and he places his left hand on
the back of the bird and the knife comes down, the body comes apart, and
he lifts the meat and he says *eat*, but my hands are folded before me, I am
kneeling, I wait – where now? – there is only darkness *eat* I open my mouth
Corpus Domini nostri his arm is round my neck he twists me to him his hair
a fiery crown *I am your king* he says, and it is dark again and I lift my eyes
to a body torn *Jesu Christi* the bread on my tongue I eat my king

ANNE **BOLEYN**
Queen of England

Beheaded after the displeasure of her husband, King Henry VIII

1536

tiny and gray is the boy and I am undone, him being no living boy and no heir to my husband, though I hold his body close and I am breathless with love for him, and the next is merely a lump of blood between my legs and he was my last chance to live, this clot this stain this wet-cleansed spot in my place of sex, but still there is my sweet girl my Elizabeth her pale face and her hair the color of the first touch of sun in the sky, the pale fire of her hair, she turns her gray eyes to me and I know I am soon to leave her and she is dressed in russet velvet and a purple satin cap with a caul of gold and the candlelight thrashes about the walls and I say to her *Lady Princess I will always be your mother* and she says in her wee voice *madam you are my Queen* and she bows as she has been taught and I ache to take her up but she is right, of course, we are who we are to each other and I am who I am to the man who must cast me off now, and I say *rise my sweet child* and she straightens and lifts her face and I bend to her, I draw near to her, I cup my daughter's head in my hands

CATHERINE **HOWARD**
Queen of England

Beheaded for adultery by Henry VIII

1542

what a tumble what a tumble rolling in the sudden dark the secret parts of
my body my own body recently giving forth blood thick and fragrant and
then, soon after, my first Henry, Henry the First, whose hands I whisper my
secrets to who touches my hidden body my self and what sweet tumblings
roll through me Henry who teaches me the flute I hold in two hands and
blow into his flute and there is music and then the dark of night in Lambeth
my step-grandmother somewhere far away in another room and I lie
dormitoried amidst the unmarried girls with great unseen puffing all about
and my own Francis, Francis the First, king of the dark, and he places his
secret inside mine and what a tumble it is breaking me in two and then
reuniting me turning me into him, and Henry my second, eighth to the
realm, his body enormous and folded into hidden places and he has parts
only I will touch, the abscess of his leg issuing forth a pale green flow *do you
not find this loathsome* he asks, softly for once, *no* I say *it is our secret*, and
my cousin Thomas whose pepper I am happy to cull pulled from the deep
earth for me to see and it destroys me at last I walk unsteady to the block
has it happened I can't remember I can't see I tumble

LADY JANE **GREY**

Queen of England for nine days

Beheaded by Queen Mary Tudor

1554

I am certain he does love me, my good John Aylmer, who teaches me
Latin and Greek and French and Italian – o cara mio – he touches with his
forefinger that hollow of bone beneath my throat and he says to me *Jane
est omnes divisa in partes tres* and I am but fourteen years upon this earth
when this love begins when John puts his fingertip beneath my throat and
his face bows slightly and the men ruffle to their knees, their faces bowed,
the crown on my head, and my brocade is gold and silver – I think only of
the dress not of the crown, which is my husband's desire and his father's – I
am not this tall but for the chopines I totter upon and I settle into the royal
barge and sail upon the dark surface of the river and all the faces of London
look and are silent Edward my king being dead his head bows and the sound
rises from his chest he touches his mouth and upon his fingertips there is a
dark red bloom and he crosses himself forehead, chest, shoulder, and then
his bloody hand passes across his throat and there is only one touch upon
my throat my sweet John naming the three parts of Jane: the heart, which
I know now is his, and the body, which has lain down already a voiceless
child upon the earth, and my head

MARY **STUART**
Queen of Scots

Beheaded by Queen Elizabeth I

1587

dark abrupt the bite at my neck gone, *sweet Jesus* I say the bite fierce upon me, my breath snarled somewhere in my chest I wait silent, my sweet Geddon inside my petticoat lays his furry throat into the bend behind my knee, the cold of the stone rises to me, hands pressing my shoulders, a veil of Corpus Christi cloth descends before my eyes, words appear about forgiveness and innocence and they are from my mouth though they might as well be from a separated head, his muzzle wetly tracing along my calf Geddon presses his wee body into my petticoat as I kneel, I stand before the stone block in the center of the Great Hall the February cold raking my breasts through my bodice scarlet the color of martyrdom, men's hands upon me roughly pulling off my gown of black satin and velvet, my throat naked now, *be gentle with the lamb* I say as he lifts the golden Agnus Dei off my neck, and my rosary, Geddon's claws clicking along at my heels I cross the stone floor refusing the arm of a man, down the great staircase my heart beating faster than Geddon's, Fotheringhay's Great Hall is below me full of upturned faces, I press him close to me his heart racing against my throat, brushing the hair from his eyes I say *there now, little man, we must see to go down these steps*

38

WALTER **RALEIGH**
Courtier and explorer

Beheaded by King James I

1618

Bess my dear old queen my Elizabeth her lips brittle her body smelling sharply beneath the clove and cinnamon from her pomander she lies next to me in the dark still besmocked though the night is warm and she has asked me here at last and I am masted for her and her bedchamber is black as pitch so she is but a shadow *no torch* she cried as I entered *upon pain of death* and now we are arranged thus my own nakedness perhaps too quick she says *call your new-found land the place of the virgin, Virginia, to honor my lifelong state* and I flinch but her smock does rise and I find the mouth of her Amazon her long fingers scrawling upon my back a history of the world *oh sir oh sir you have found the city of gold at last* she says, knowing me well this fills my sails the jungles of ancient lands are mine my queen *oh swisser swatter* she cries and falls away and I lie beside her staring into the dark, and I am sated certainly, but the moment calls for some new thing, and I say *wait, my queen* and I am out her door to the nearest torch and I have already prepared the treasure from my new world, this sweet sotweed this tobacco, and I sail back and slip in beside her and we sit and we smoke

BRITA **GULLSMED**
Swedish woman

Beheaded for alleged witchcraft

1675

night has come and curls about my head and stays and sleeps a long sleep, for months here on the edge of the taiga I rise to trim the lamp and Margit leaps silently up and rubs her chin on my knuckle she is not an imp of Satan my black cat but she is not of these others either, these humans I am one of, I lie down in the darkness of my bed and once again there is a man and I am safely that to the world, the woman beside him, he lies heavy upon me raking my face with his beard and beating my loins and cursing the ashen soil he turns and cursing my barren womb and I am of him he says but I cannot draw a breath and I do not know him and he is gone to molder in the ground and now Margit leaps upon my chest and she tramps softly there drooling and murmuring to me and I lay my hands upon her fur and we purr together and I am this cat and through her I am the spruce and the pine standing all about and I am the moon-glint of the ice and the drifting of the snow and the cry of the wolf and she lays her face against mine and I am the scattered white fire of the stars and I am the long long night

LOUIS XVI

King of France

Guillotined by order of the French Revolutionary Tribunal

1793

thrash and flurry in the undergrowth a bird a boar a stag the rush of wings of legs I lift a Charleville to my shoulder the musket cool to my hands I squeeze the trigger and feel heavily that half heartbeat of silence and then the cry and the kick of her, the night my bed I shudder the trees nearby I am alone at wood's edge *be a man* the king my father says but I am not a man and I feel the beast there invisible in the dark – the Beast of Gévaudan – he is far from Paris but he steps from the woods before me a wolf as big as a lion a hundred dead in the countryside he has passed by the animals of the field to savage a man or woman or child and he faces me and he lifts his ragged muzzle to the sky and howls *liberty to kill, equality of death, fraternity of beasts* and I wake and I am still a child my king's horsemen are off slogging through the marshes of the Auvergne to find him but he is with me and I am king now and I pass the smoking musket to my man who hands me another and I shoot and shoot again and again and the bird falls and the boar and the stag but behind me is the beast and he seizes me by the head

MARIE ANTOINETTE
Queen of France

Guillotined by order of the French Revolutionary Tribunal

1793

softly on the arm he touches his wife and they hesitate in the dim corridor I a few steps behind holding tight to nurse's petticoat and I know how never never again will I be present in a moment like this because there is always the great goose-flock of my brothers and sisters and always there are courtiers and ladies-in-waiting and I am but a little girl a little little girl with a lute I can play and satin shoes with such elegant thin soles I feel the cold stone on my toes and he touches his wife's arm, he who is Emperor of Austria, King of Jerusalem, Hungary, Bohemia, Dalmatia, Croatia, and even more, that's as far as I can remember, I am small as small can be I could crawl into the belly of my lute and stay there looking between the strings he touches his wife's arm and he is my father and she is my mother the Empress of Austria and Queen of Jerusalem and Hungary and so forth and her skirts are bright and enormous I could live inside them and bring my three dogs and my pony too and all my clothes and the skirts are a problem for my father who has touched my mother's arm because he leans far over far across them and nearly falls but she turns her face to him knowing he is her beloved and he kisses her

MARIE-JEANNE **BÉCU**
(COMTESSE DU BARRY)
Mistress to King Louis XV

Guillotined by order of the French Revolutionary Tribunal

1793

snow is falling the Seine runs with ice and I come in from the cold my face tingling I climb the narrow stairs Monsieur Gluck pushing past me descending and humming some bit of sad music and I am led by the elbow and now I am beside his bed, Monsieur Voltaire, and he takes my hand and draws it to his face and the tip of his long nose touches my knuckle as his lips kiss my fingers and his breath is labored like my King I sit beside Louis and I cannot see the pox upon him in the dark but his breath drags itself heavily through his body and I bend to him and whisper *my Lord the child you lately took to your bed has done this to you* and my hand falls upon his wrist and squeezes hard and Monsieur Voltaire lifts his face from my hand and there is a faint stain of blood at the corner of his lip and he narrows his eyes at me *we are merely at a play, my dear* he says and I ask *is it true there is no place beyond, where the King will hold me again* and he says *whether there is a heaven and hell or not, I am afraid you are finished with Louis* and only as I speak do I understand why it is I reply *then all is for the best*

ANTOINE-LAURENT **LAVOISIER**
Scientist

Guillotined by order of the French Revolutionary Tribunal

1794

air and fire, I breathe deep upon a shore in Brittany and the sun is falling into the sea before my eyes but I am full of thoughts, the ideas of things beyond my sight – the essence of fire is matter fusing with oxygen – a flame from a candle by my bed this vast orb of sun the torch lighting the way past iron doors my wrists shackled my time come my breath guttering like a flame, these are all one, the welter of the sun the welter in my chest, I have proved this also – to burn, to breathe are the same process – the oxygen of the air rushes inside the furnace of my lungs and it flares I give off heat I dress Monsieur Seguin in a suit of taffeta and elastic gum and I seal his mouth with putty and his breath comes and goes through my instruments through my mind he lives he burns we carry our own small sun inside us and not a particle of mass is lost nothing is lost we fuse we are carried off to another state my father-in-law moves ahead of me along the corridor and now he lays down his head on the instrument and the blade falls the head falls one fire goes out and another begins and nothing is lost on a shore in Brittany the sun vanishes but the seams of cloud flare up before me

ANDRÉ **CHÉNIER**

Poet

Guillotined by order of the French Revolutionary Tribunal

1794

great the minds in Mother's gilded chairs, Lavoisier and David and Suvée, and along the edge of our salon the heavy scent of women, lavender and jasmine and the smell of their bodies, and the mounting of powdered hair that falls now about the shoulders of the Duchess of Fleury who kissed Mother's cheeks and me full on the mouth and asked *are you truly a man* and *who here is a poet*, dull-eyed now she drifts near our jailer who palms her breast and she pauses as if in thought and he lets her pass, *Lavoisier is gone to the blade* whispers Suvée who has bribed for paints, and I sit for him in a slant of light from the high window and he lifts his brush and tells me to stop trembling, the stone hall full of our kind our lace filthy the turnkeys lifting their red Phrygian caps to cheer the reading of tomorrow's condemned, and in my cell my hands will not stop quaking nor my chest nor my knees when I try to stand and I pace and I wait for my own brush my own paint as words pass through my head in a death cart, iron wheels turning on the cobbles, they pass to the scaffold and are lost, but now: at last, my quill, my ink, a basket full of dirty clothes, my words are hid within, *I am* and *I am*

MAXIMILIEN **ROBESPIERRE**

Lawyer and revolutionary

Guillotined by the Revolutionary Convention

1794

Father dressed immaculately his knee breeches his silk stockings his tailcoat Mother dead in the parlor her arms folded across her chest he leans against the far wall and I am trying to get my arms around Augustin and Charlotte and Henriette they seem like children to me now, my brother and my sisters, though I am myself only six years on this earth I try to hold them my arms straining and inadequate and I know already that the man leaning there is dead to us too and I am responsible and now the door shuts hard the knocker clangs he has said nothing I follow quickly and strain at the door and he is gone his horse clatters away and he is gone the Bois de Boulogne is full of citizens dressed innocently in tricolor trousers and clogs and red caps I walk among them my hound at my side the summer daylight lingering and they look to me and I want to open my arms they are children and there are many who would harm them and I am in my room above the carpentry yard the sky incarnate with dawn my words prepared at last for the Convention and I dress in white silk stockings and knee breeches and floral waistcoat and black tailcoat and red cravat and my hair is powdered and on the cobbles a scaffold and the blade, dear father, for us all

PIERRE-FRANÇOIS **LACENAIRE**
Criminal and memoirist

Guillotined for murder

1836

slim at hip and thigh my lover my fiancée my guillotine but her opening is large, large enough for me to give her everything my head sliding inside her, she is tall and she is painted crimson not mere lips and cheeks but all over my sweet woman – her narrow shoulders, her arms held primly to her side, her lap that I will fling myself upon – all her thin body is rouged for me, all but her bosom which is naked and unadorned, polished bright, her sharp-edged tit that waits for me and has always waited for me, I pass her in the street in a blood dawn and she will soon give herself to another man – she is no virgin, my fiancée, I am reconciled to her past with others – and this first moment I see her I stagger to a stop I am but a boy a petty thief and my father is at my side his mustache waxed into rapier points he lifts his hand toward the lady and says *that is where you will end* and cuffs the back of my head and I am betrothed and I come to her no virgin I put my own blade deep inside a widow she moans though it is but a boy's affair to prepare me for my worldly lover: I stand before her now I bow I slide I enter her and I await her ferocious embrace

TA CHIN
Chinese wife

Beheaded by her husband

1838

straight and whole are my feet I would rise and run as I have loved for many
winkings of the moon to run with my brothers but I press my feet side by
side and wiggle my toes this last time and whisper to them *goodbye* I know
what is before me my mother in the courtyard singing prayers to Kuan Yin
the goddess of mercy, not to spare me a life of pain but to wither my feet
to perfection, the mercy of the golden lotus, the mercy of a wealthy man
to keep me, I tremble I am ready to weep but for these tiny stones of anger
Kuan Yin has placed in the corners of my eyes even as the foot-binder puts
the soaking tub before me that first night even as my husband trembles
before me in the torch light trembling always from the opium but this night
he trembles from what he believes about the brushing of my sleeve by a man
he himself brought to our house and my mother sings and my toes are seized
and folded hard under and the wrappings wind and wind and squeeze and
my arch cracks and I see Buddha in heaven sitting on his lotus but it is my
naked foot the golden lotus he sits upon and hands push me down my neck
made bare and I cry *please, before my head cut off my feet*

JACOB
American slave

Beheaded by his owner

1855

sowbelly frying in the first coming-up light I smell it being only a child my Sukey-mammy whisper me about how my own from-her-body mammy done been sold away but she still loves me the morning bell ringing on some other plantation far off Sukey-mammy singing *my way's cloudy go send them angels down* our own morning bell ringing and I am a strong-back man and the driver beats me bullwhip fire, now across my right side, now across my left, and another day he beats me, and another, my back always on fire, clearing some new part of the forest for corn and for cotton the chopping done and the grubbing and the log heaps piled and burning filling the night sky with flame, and I know something burning in me and Sukey lying in the dirt the driver nudging her at the shoulder with his boot cause she tell a child how he have a soul of his own and that night I am rushing and my thumbs dig deep in the driver's throat and I lay a torch to a hayrick the sky going hot as a bullwhip lash behind me the hounds calling and I am running hard through corn row and forest and I am a child and I walk just a little ways from my Sukey to the window and I see the first fire of dawn and a bell is ringing far off somewhere

ANGRY EYES

Apache warrior

Beheaded by Mexican troops

1880

breechcloth and moccasins only these things on my body and my head
bound by a cloth band my face and chest and arms stained but I do not
know the colors I do not look, my eyes are fixed on the horizon beyond
mesquite and piñon and stone and I am ready to fight though I have no bow
no arrow not even the rifle, I bend to the white man in dark blue, the first to
die by my hand, and I listen for his spirit nearby, his hair the color of flame
his face filled with tiny faded spots painted there perhaps to call upon the
stars his mouth open voiceless my arrow through the center of his chest I put
my hand on the stock of his rifle, still listening but there is nothing no bird
no insect – *where are you, my foe?* – and the sun is setting and my hands
are empty and I dance, like a woman I dance with mincing steps my elbows
held close against me my face impassive before the fading light, the edge of
the world is the color of old blood, my body dances stealthily all my flesh
trembling to an unheard drum and I am alone in this place, but no, his spirit
whispers he is beside me now, in breechcloth and moccasins, and we dance
barely moving nearly touching I and this white man with hair of flame

CHIN CHIN **CHAN**
Student

Beheaded by Chinese authorities for maintaining a romantic correspondence with an American girl he met while studying in the USA

1882

moon no longer a blossom a pearl a lantern in a lover's door but a bodiless face, mine, in a train window, she on the platform trying not to look at me directly, as if she were there for someone else, and the train hurtles in the dark and I stare into the stars and not even a poet could find the moon in this sky not even Li Po in a boat with quill and ink in hand he searches this night sky and then looks at me from across the water and shrugs and I am the cicada, seventeen at last, my skin splits open and I emerge a perfect man ready to sing but there is so little time and the song I hear in return fades in the grind of these engines, I sit with my own quill and ink, the cicadas singing in the courtyard outside, *my dear Elizabeth my love* these words I write blur before my eyes even as she draws near, the smell of lavender the low trill of her laughter and then a sigh *you sweet boy what are we to do* she says and I put my hand on hers and I float above in the dark and I see Li Po in his boat and he leans far out over the water opening his arms to embrace the severed head of a moon and he tips forward and vanishes

DAVE **RUDABAUGH**
Outlaw and briefly member of Billy the Kid's gang

Beheaded by townspeople in Parral, Mexico

1886

ready now to throw down on me some old Johnny Reb calls me out and I'm young and twitchy and into my hand comes my 1860 Colt Army my first sweet thing walnut in my palm black powder and paper-wrapped cartridges eight-inch barrel coming out and it's been around a long time and knows what to do the bluing near all rubbed off but you can see the big-masted ships etched on the cylinder the Texas navy blowing up the Mexicans their dark faces around me hands grabbing and a later Colt in my hand my Peacemaker barks like a stable dog a fat Mex flying back from the table his sombrero spattered from my bullet in his brain and Billy touches my shoulder, the Kid is dead but there are his eyes, as blue as noonday, and his tiny hand on my shoulder, he has the smallest damn hands, like a girl, Billy whispers *let's ride* and I lift my hand to touch his and I'm holding my first Colt all sassy and sweet and long and it thumps and kicks and goes hot and Johnny Reb is falling backward, my first kill, and I say to him *here's me*, and all at once I see my life ahead my hand full of pistol my trigger finger touchy as my cock and I'm riding hard and I'm lying under the stars and Billy's sleeping nearby quiet as a girl

AGNES GWENLAN

Factory girl

Decapitated by elevator

1889

quarry sounds, the thump and boom all day, the dishes rattle and Mama flinches each time with Papa out there breaking up the mountain and then he and my uncles are by the fire and they sing and I huddle into sleep *ar hyd y nos* they sing *all through the night* and I am curled on a straw mattress stacked with a hundred others belowdecks the ocean out in the dark all around us and Mama lies above me I can hear her crying for my father crushed by falling slate, a quarryman's death, Miss Liberty watches us sail by, her torch lifted in the twilight, and it suddenly flares into electric light and we gasp and cheer and we sit in the harbor, the city on one hand and Ellis Island on the other, a basket goes over the side and up comes a strange new thing bananas I would eat one skin and all but for a man with quarry hands bending near and peeling it for me and I eat and it is good and he is gone and we are in an open trolley, Mama and I, and we are carried up Broadway beneath buildings higher than mountains and harder than slate and the tenement is dark and surrounds us like the sea and he sings softly in my ear *sleep my love and peace attend thee* and I whisper *all right Papa all right*

CHARLES H. **STUART**

Texas farmer

Beheaded by his two teenage daughters

1904

underfoot the pine board cricks, I pause and let it die, I want to go in quiet, the dark and the chill are coming up under my nightshirt and I'm skittish feeling the dangle of my parts I'm moving along again bobbling and churning down there, the door is closed I come near and I palm the knob which is cool as the curve of their shoulders I turn the knob softly but now they're sitting in sunlight in the kitchen their mama working the water pump in the yard, them both side by side, my daughters, come from my flesh, and Wilhelmina is old enough to look at me that way – the stare that don't flicker – the woman-stare like her mama but without the prattle and the complaints – Valmer not yet with the stare, her eyes still restless like some other women I know – and the pine board cricks under my step and I keep on to the doorknob and I touch it and it's cold and I turn it and the pine board cricks and I slide on along and my hand goes to the doorknob and it is serious cold to the touch – no, not cold at all – it's hot it's searing hot my hand is fixing to torch up but I can't let go and from under the door comes the smell of sulphur and I know it's not them inside, it's what's next for me

ROKHEL **POGORELSKY**

Jewish woman

Beheaded in Russian pogrom

1905

taste of horseradish taste of nettle I draw the covers tight about me the trees beyond the dark window lash in the wind my brother nearby weeps against his will *sorry Papa sorry* and beneath the wind my father's voice tumbles *Pinchas be still the blood was on the doorpost* the lambs in the field raise their head to a hollow sound the soles of my feet quake *our sons were spared* father says to Pinchas but in the field I hear horses and I have my own first son on my back my Aron and I turn from the sound of hooves and I run across the field that rolls beneath me twisting at my ankles I look behind and the men on horses stay on the road a dozen Cossacks in high boots and billowing trousers and one turns his face toward me I run hard and they go on toward the village and I follow the hedge line and through a stand of water oaks and Aron begins to cry his tiny hands plucking at my ears *be still* I say and my cottage now my husband gone a lashing in my chest like trees in a wind and a basket by the step, I put my son inside, my shawl on top, for when this all is done another must find him: a scythe nearby, I cut my hand and spill my blood upon the door

JOHN MARTIN
Boy

*Decapitated by subway after lifting sidewalk grate and falling onto
the tracks below*

1921

Babe oh Babe hit it all the way out here Babe and jumping jimjams he's
done it the ball lifting up like a Fourth of July rocket but not exploding just
keeping on going up and coming my way out here in the right-field bleachers
and all the Polo Grounds Johnnies around me losing their bowlers falling on
themselves and there's a rush from the dark and steel on my throat and the
nickel rolls perfect on its edge and we're all real quiet my friends and me and
down it goes into the grate and down I go into the dark after it and down
I go falling to the track I can get up now but something's happened to my
arms and legs they're flimsy loose and too light to lift and it's only jostling
shoulders and elbows and sweat beads flying and hats tumbling and I fight
clear and Babe's thirty-first of the year is falling from the sky rushing at me
oh Babe the orphan boy oh Babe smoking a cigar in his tweedy cap a few
weeks ago he comes out of the stadium trailing smoke and I got nothing for
him to sign but the back of my hand and this time I'll take him a ball but
all of a sudden it dies and falls a few rows in front of me Babe signs my skin
and puts his hand on my head

HENRI **LANDRU**

Second-hand furniture dealer, also known as the "Bluebeard of Gambais"

Guillotined for the murder of ten women

1922

parlor mirrors are hard to sell when flawed like this one, tinting my beard the color of a bruise, I clap my hand over the bristled hair and turn to this woman but her deer's eyes are blind to my beard, seeing only my sympathetic gaze, and her face is traced with age and her upper lip is furred and her husband is long dead and her hands are brittle from scrubbing and she is worse than dead as a widow, her money useless to her, the newspapers were right I am spinning from Mother Goose's mouth – the young wife choking back her disgust at my blue beard, which, however, I do not shave, and I go off giving her all the chateau's keys and warning her on pain of death not to enter the cellar room, the room where I have secretly placed the disassembled bodies of seven wives, the room that yields only to this small key, which, however, I do not simply withhold from her – my hands quicken I kiss Madame's furred lip and she cries out in pleasure and the deal is struck, a moment of passion she would never have had, for the dead man's settee and his four-poster bed and his commode and his wife's head lying upon its pillow and this cleaver in my hand and I cut through and hold it up, her eyes still blinking, and I kiss her trembling lips

PAUL **GORGULOFF**
Russian immigrant to France

Guillotined for assassinating French President Paul Doumer at charity book signing

1932

silver rivets all around I step into the rocket Paul Gorguloff space pilot who turns to Professor Oberth and shakes his hand I am to fly his rocket to the moon and I step from the rocket the rivets scorched black and great crowds of people press in crying *tell us your story* and I sit before the window and I take up my fine pen and the pistol is on my desk and a sheaf of blank paper and I post the cap of my Mont Blanc and I write *Memoirs of Paul Gorguloff* and the pages tumble from me Paul Gorguloff the writer paces the floor the carpet worn through the desk overflowing I am in a crowd now that clamors for books and they are fools not recognizing the greatness moving among them my pen clipped in my shirt pocket and Claude Farrère – a novelist unworthy to wipe my dripping nib – sits signing and I deign to buy his *Useless Hands* about breadmakers in the distant future replaced by robot hands and he autographs my book with a cheap pen and I turn the book and I uncap my Mont Blanc before his eyes and I sign it above his name *Paul Gorguloff the man who killed the President of the French Republic* Paul Doumer at another table signing his books thinking himself a writer and the pistol is in my hand and I critique his work

BENITA **VON BERG**
German baroness

Beheaded by Adolf Hitler for espionage

1935

dying tip of one cigarette I touch to another, my cell at Plötzensee is full of
tobacco smoke and I fill my lungs holding very still, woolen socks on my feet
prison trousers and shirt if I could but whiten my face and trace my lips in
scarlet we lean together and sing Brecht the club full of smoke and bodies
the emcee in tails and white tie points at me – *welcome to Kabarett madam
but free that red fox about your neck he is our comrade* – and it is Munich
now a woman in a swirl of silk, her body naked beneath, she leaps onto our
table and her womansmell fills my lungs I leave my cigarette in my mouth
my hand falling the sound of weeping from some other cell I slip my hand
inside these rough trousers to my own cleft like hers flashing above me on
the table and her face is white her lips scarlet and Friedrichstrasse is ablaze
with electric light passing in a cab his clumsy Polish hand between my legs I
whisper *Captain, your country is in danger,* as if I loved him, and our voices
swell through the smoke and we sing *there was a time and now it's all gone
by* and I move down the corridor into the room of the ax and the executioner
turns to greet me and he is dressed in tails and white tie *welcome*

NGUYEN VAN **TRINH**

Viet Minh guerrilla leader

Guillotined by French Colonial authorities

1952

very still, I hold my rifle hard against my chest and I am careful even in the breath I draw I am folded against a mangrove tree my knees tucked close I move my eyes but I can see none of my comrades and of course I cannot hear them for we all wait on the noisy French wait till they are between the two columns of us and I should at least be able to see my friend Ky I know his place forward in a closing of vines but he is not there and I wait for the French and I think of my father in his collar and cravat and the way his head would draw down like a tortoise when he spoke of the Frenchman who ran his lycée *pull your collar off, my father, seize by the throat that man who shames you* and my father is a vase of ashes and my mother prays in the bourgeois myth that his spirit lives yet in another realm, and I hear them nearby, breaking dry leaves beneath their feet, and it is time and I make a sharp bird cry and I leap now but there is no rifle in my hands I have come from the trees onto the path and these are not Frenchmen but Vietnamese in mandarin dress and one turns his face and it is my father and he offers his hand

ALWI **SHAH**
Yemeni executioner

Beheaded for a crime unrelated to his work

1958

rising slow from a low place I see a row of heads sitting before me on a stone wall ear-to-ear arrayed beyond my sight to either side, I face them and their eyes turn to me and I hear the stirring of feet all around me, a jumbled huddling-in of bodies naked and battered with bones cracked and bulging knots and blooms of bruise and crusted lappings of blood, how I loved you all, loved righteously snapping the cords of all your lives, and so you come to taunt me but praise Allah I have done his holy work and I took as his sign the trill of sweetness that came upon me in this my work and now I turn and look into the stone-shattered face of Haleema Alsakkaf an adultering woman and she holds in her right hand the head of Akram Alshami her lover who, like the others, moves his eyes to me and I say *praise Allah you have paid righteously* and she says *praise Allah who we call the one God and who loves his creatures, we are sent as you knew us but we are restored in heaven* and I see now that my own head hangs in her left hand and I cry *praise Allah he will have mercy on me also* and she says *the mercy of God seeks sinful love before righteous hatred* and I wait for my head to fall

CHICKEN

Americauna pullet

Beheaded in Alabama for Sunday dinner

1958

little grit things in the straw here and I peck and peck and they're gone and I go over there a wormy thing but it's a leaf stem which I always grab but it never goes mush like an actual worm which I look and look and listen for and the flying ones come down and they walk among us and they cock their heads and hear the slither in the earth and they grab and up one comes but after a rain it's good for me the worms come up and I run here and I run there and I eat and the grit is good too over there I go for grit though the soft slither is even better but it's dry now dry all around and they are vanished, wait, wait, the rest of me is gone and from beyond the wire from past the dog-leap from down the long ruts I can hear a muttery cluckering and it is like when I broke at last from the eggy wall and into the light and a fluff of feathers hovered near and made this same sound but this muckery wuckering is vast, this at last is the hen who fills the sky, and I am rushing now along the path and the clucking is for me and it is very loud and a great wide road is suddenly before me and she is beyond and I cross

VERA JAYNE **PALMER**
(STAGE NAME, JAYNE MANSFIELD)
Actress

Decapitated in car crash

1967

faint his face his eyes but I feel the soft run of his hand on my hair I am so tiny I am so much his little Vera that I am breathless I put my arms across his chest my father and I listen to the draw of his breath and he is gone and I am before these faces upturned I could open my arms and not get round them all I am their Jayne I am their Miss Freeway I am their Miss Electric Switch and Miss Photoflash and Miss Geiger Counter I am their Miss Pure Maple Syrup I am the wide clean road to where they want to go and I am the thing you touch to turn on the light and I am the bright caught moment and I am the crackle of invisible fire that will burn the very flesh from your bones and I am sweet beyond all bearing and pure and I am Chanel Number Five I sit in the quiet in a dressing room before the eyes will turn to me and I touch the scent to my skin and suddenly I am the smell of jasmine and of orange blossom and if you concentrate harder I am rose and iris and lily-of-the-valley and if you wait I am amber and patchouli and vanilla and he puts his face in my hair and he breathes in and he says *how sweet*

LE VAN **KY**
Hue city official

Beheaded by North Vietnamese troops

1968

blossoms floating on the Perfume River plumeria and mango and lychee the water itself smelling of mountain flowers even after the blossoms have eddied away I drag my hand in the river my father pulling at the oar and he says my name sharply *Ky* and I take up my own oar again and now we loll in the sun beside the South China Sea my father sleeping my mother huddling against my sister and speaking low and I wander away back toward the river far along the edge of the lagoon and even though there is no one in sight my heart is already beating furiously and the jungle closes in and around a bend she is crouched by the river's edge and I cut toward the tree line before she knows to look up, I circle and I creep close, her back is to me and she must be a peasant girl her skin is dark from the sun and her shirt clings to her, her naked back shines through the thin wet cloth, and she angles her head and pours the river into her long midnight hair, once, and again, and she has stolen my breath and she sits back and shakes her wet hair and I watch, never seeing her face, then she rises and goes away forever, and I understand: though the blossoms pass along in the current and vanish the river still smells sweet

KIMITAKE **HIRAOKA**
(PEN NAME, YUKIO MISHIMA)

Japanese novelist

*Beheaded at his own request by a paramilitary colleague as he committed
ritual disembowelment after failing to persuade Japan's Self-Defense Forces
to overthrow the government*

1970

Tokyo roiling in flames like the sea my young man's body too frail to find
a patriot's death I am a watcher shaping words already from the roof of
the arsenal my wrists thin my arms a girl's arms the American bombers
invisible in the scarlet smoke of the night sky, the flames now inside my
body, brought there by my own hand, my own sword, my samurai arm –
no, vanished now – no body at all – but words, always words, only words,
which are my coward's sword – and I call the flames to return, to fill the sky
with bombs, take the salarymen sleeping on commuter trains take the shops
filled with breakfast cereal and French perfume and vacuum cleaners take
the politicians who yield our swords, who make our Emperor the English
queen, rise up, my country grown girlish and frail, my face grows hot from
the flames of Tokyo and from shame at my body and then ten thousand
confrontations before a gymnasium mirror and my arms thicken my thighs
muscled carrying me to an act, I am breathless with power the rising sun
tied round my head I stand before our warriors, our past, and they laugh at
a girlish boychild and the city lies quiet against the night the horizon filling
not with flame but with words, with manuscripts, I have named myself after
snow I have been cold all along I am only a writer

ROBERT **KORNBLUTH**

Senior partner in advertising firm

Decapitated by elevator

1984

look I cry: SHE CLOSED, THE DOOR, RIGHT IN YOUR FACE, THE WHISKERS
SIR, YOU MUST ERASE, BURMA SHAVE swept by my headlights, *there, I wrote
those words*, my hands clenched tight on the wheel, the wrong thing to say
she is quiet beside me quaking and weeping in rage and I yearn for a no
more tears formula, *I give the best to you each morning* I say *it takes a wife
to know the difference between Hanes and just underwear*, surely I'm not
speaking these words to Anne the long-suffering Anne my wife once my wife
long ago we are in a brand new 1952 Packard – ask the man who owns one
– long before this present darkness came upon me – is it possible? panties
more comfortable than wearing nothing? – Anne naked by the window in a
luxury suite, affordable comfort, *no more tears* I say, *do you know me* she
says, *what we have is the real thing* I say, and she is gone I dream of her and
she is wearing her Maidenform Bra and my mouth brims with words that I
know will do only harm – would you offer a Tiparillo to a lady? – a cigarette
at least, outside the lawyer's office, mellow, an aid to digestion, we smoke
and we stay silent and she sighs and is gone, DON'T LOSE, YOUR HEAD, TO
GAIN A MINUTE, YOU NEED YOUR HEAD, YOUR BRAINS ARE IN IT

JENNIFER HADLEY

Marketing director

Decapitated in car crash

1989

overhead jet engines the phone rings and a flash of landing lights outside, the chocolate mint still on my pillow, I know who it is, *hello* I say, *hello* he says, *I'm just down the hall* he says, *I know* I say, *are we going to do this* he says, a statement, my husband has called already to say goodnight and I say *your wife's call, just finished* he says, I don't say that I'm having trouble holding the phone to my ear I am so weak in the limbs breathless, overhead jet engines the phone rings a flash of light beyond the window a jet rushing back to earth from somewhere the chocolate on my pillow *hello* I say, *hello I'm just down the hall* he says, *I know* I say, *are we going to do this* he says, the phone rings a sound like ice falling from the eaves jet engines overhead my husband standing thigh-high in snow just beyond our patio his breath pluming and ice falling between us and then he waves *did it snow* I ask him tonight, *yes* he says *but the ice is worse the wires are down there is no electricity no heat*, I say *goodnight*, the line rasping with his thrown kiss, I put the receiver in the cradle, I pick up the chocolate I put it down, jet engines overhead the phone rings there is a knock at my door

NICOLE **BROWN SIMPSON**

California woman

Decapitated by assailant

1994

running hard along Venice Beach the clutch of breakers around my feet I run against the pull and I've come to this, to a place of jasmine smell and sea and car exhaust and stucco walls and Hollywood spelled across a mountain, and I run easily with the question *what can I be*, I've got great legs he says, and he should know because he runs for a living I love to see him run though he says I don't really understand but I do I run with him each time he holds something private in his arm and all the others rush to bring him down but he cuts and jukes and surges: run now, my children, run down the hall and close your doors because I cannot, his sweet slick child's face in the faces of my children, such beautiful skin I draw my hand tender along his cheek and he closes his eyes the moon out there rising I am large with her inside me, my child, and glass shatters and the bones of my face vibrate and my teeth all hurt I draw my hand along my cheek I think to try to run and he rushes up fast and I can see what's tucked there in the crook of his arm and it is me, it is my head, and I stare into my own eyes and I know the answer always was *his wife*

MOHAMMED AZIZ **NAJAFI**

Iraqi Shiite cleric

Beheaded by Saddam Hussein

1996

barren ground but holy, this plateau before me, trampled smooth by the feet of millions, the true people of Allah, but empty now though it is Hajj and the Mount of Mercy is behind me I feel its press between my shoulder blades and the pilgrims should be everywhere but the ground is beaten into silence and there is no one – *oh Allah leave me not alone* – for I have no seed but your holy words, I have no family but the family of your great people, no child but your revealed way, I would summon the millions cloaked in white so I could be among them and we would cry out as one *Allah I have responded to you* I am draped in seamless cotton I am barefoot and I am penitent, and the echo of my prayers is still in my head I have been silent only the briefest of moments and I yearn for the tumult of my brothers in Allah I would kneel and touch my face to this long-beaten ground as one with a million other faces, but no, I am standing upright and I am alone and before me now there is only a desert tamarisk, feathery pink, the merest growing thing and it catches the sun as if it is on fire and I hear a voice say to me *it is time now to take thy only son and cut his throat*

LYDIA **KOENIG**

Chicago woman

Decapitated by her son

1999

baby Mama calls me baby on my lap a lump of cloth baby doll and then a freckled face, Howdy Doody baby, I hum his name his puppet strings folded under, not a doll but I like his hard legs and arms beneath his clothes like real bones, Lake Michigan at twilight the color of tarnished brass a hand inside my lap and he asks me that night atop the Prudential Building the lake too dark to see and then my baby my own baby boy his bones deep and untouchable inside him, I dress him in pink thinking it makes no difference I hold him baby and then in plaid and he has freckles on his nose and he stinks of urine from his bed I carry the great lump of soiled cloth and the Tide waiting, the cleaning power of Tide and Oxydol and Clorox, and the man is gone and my baby cries all night through, though he is no baby he is returned and he says *help me find a vein help me tap this vein* and I cannot, I take his load of piss sheets to the Maytag in the basement and it is cool here and smells of the lake on a bad day and I wash them and dry them sitting in the dimness of the basement and I hold these sheets in my lap my baby my baby's voice is behind me

CLAUDE **MESSNER**

Homeless man

Decapitated by Amtrak train after laying his neck on the track

2000

no oh no not him again from the rush of a fucking train I get the old man, what's taking that goddam train so long it was here a moment ago, maybe it's lying on its side jumped by a penny on the track I hide in the weeds and my shiny Lincoln-head is out there waiting for the Illinois Central from Chicago and I know I should be thinking about the careening of the engine the flight of the baggage car into the trees but all I've got is him whipping off his belt to do me, the sonofabitch, he disappears for a week only to come back for this, and I can't fucking believe I'm lifting my hand trying to take his, we're walking along storefronts I'm barely taller than the fire plugs and I'm trying to take that hand and it flicks like at a housefly, and later on there's a long while, a few years, of just me and my mother and she likes her young man she runs her finger through the great front wave of my hair, and then he's back and he's about breaking my arm and I'm in a barber's chair and I can see my beautiful duck's ass of a do in the mirror and I whisper to the barber *please just a little around the edges* and my dad says *buzz him, buzz him up clean, take it all off*

71

LOIS **KENNERLY**
Systems analyst

Beheaded in collapse of the south tower of the World Trade Center
2001

oh my god oh my god Paul Anka is looking at me now even as he sings he bends down from the stage and his hand comes out asking me to rise to go up there with him and I am next to him dazzled by the lights the crowd roaring his voice near my face *squeeze me oh so tight* and his arm comes around me I am sixteen and now I am twenty and we step out the side door of the church hall and no one has noticed us go, me in my bridal dress and Sam in his tux, and we crouch flat-footed near the door like you see the Vietnamese do on TV and we smoke and I've just married him but this is the moment I know I love him for sure, us smoking outside alone, and the snow is falling beyond my window I have awakened and I know it's time for my baby she's ready though my water hasn't broken and I'm not in any pain I know this is the day and it's still snowing beyond the hospital window the flakes look big as her hands and she's taking my milk and Sam is singing *you're having my baby* and I think him a damn fool, she's mine, and I can hardly see, the lights are so bright, and an arm slips around my waist *put your head on my shoulder*

72

ISIOMA **OWOLABI**

Woman of Bani, Burkina Faso

Beheaded by fatwa

2002

Mother I cannot see your face I walk beside you too young to veil my own
but I yearn for your eyes, surely I can see my mother's eyes even in public,
let the men turn their own eyes away for my sake, but behind us are the nine
mosques that have risen from the earth and their veined walls are beneath
our feet, the desiccated road, for father takes us east to a purer love of Allah,
and his back is to me – no – he has turned round, in Nigeria, I am nearly a
woman, the veil drops upon my face, he whispers that I live now where the
road has ended on the cliff's edge and if I lift this thing between me and the
world I will lose my balance and fall to my death, so my mother will never
see my eyes again in sunlight, and there is a great rushing about me now, she
lies dead and veiled and I slip into the night and the moonlight falls upon
my naked eyes, my hand in the hand of a man whose body is unveiled and
his part rises like a mosque of Bani, and I speak to the world a gentle truth
about the prophet and the dark swims upon me I hurtle back along the road
to the mosques of my home where I know that heaven is simply a shaping
of the earth

HANADI TAYSEER **JARADAT**

Law student

Beheaded by self-detonation of shaheed-belt suicide bomb

2003

I am heavy with child praise Allah I am at last with child my head is full of the law that I am permitted to study to serve our people but I have not forgotten my greater destiny praise Allah I am also with child, the words of the Prophet – peace be upon him – saying *Paradise lies at the feet of mothers*, I have not forgotten, I move across rubbled ground and my baby is pressed hard against my womb wait wait my face is naked my head is bare I touch where my baby is and he is very heavy ten kilos and his bones are large and hard and stacked side by side his cord winds secretly into the pocket of the jeans that bind my legs my loins I wear the clothes of harlots my hand is on his private part I am but to press there, my baby placed in me by a man with his face covered I turn my head and open my cloak to a man I do not know, an angel of Allah surely, his arms around me and my baby is suddenly holding me tight I am moving in a room full of people cursed by Allah my baby heavy against me surely he has eyes and a mouth and a heart, a woman nearby damned but large with child, I have my own, I touch him and he cries out

EARL **DAGGETT**

Laid-off Mississippi heavy-equipment operator

Beheaded by his lover's husband

2003

Elmer, that economy-size coon turd who is my friend, points his shotgun straight up over his dang head – and mine, if you please, I'm standing right next to him – and he goes and does this so fast I ain't got time to jump away from sharing his rightly earned fate, he pulls the trigger fixing to kill a squirrel and instead of bringing buckshot and tree limbs and small-animal guts raining down on our heads, like ought to be the outcome, he plumb misses the whole tree and falls backwards – he's got that bad a damn aim – and likewise his thumbs is always about hammered to pulp whenever it's time to tarpaper his barn or fix a porch plank, and he don't even deserve the love of Maisie who has billowy warm thighs and Elmer probably can't even manage to get it into her honey pot, not with both hands on his pecker and a red flag flying between her legs, so I figure I'm okay as I open one eye and it's only half past two and he should be at the planing mill and Maisie is still snoring like a rotary saw beside me and I jump up and grab my pants to make one clean leap: here I go right now I am so light and graceful like a greyhound at the track I'll just leap through that window and be clean plumb away from his ax

MAISIE **HOBBS**

Mississippi woman

Beheaded by her husband

2003

night that's dark as fresh tar on the county road we roll through our trailer park late from Wednesday church and I rest my chin on our Chevy's door and one lit window after another goes by Mandy Lou leaning into Henry him putting his arms around her and shadows going up and down beside the flicker of Lila's TV and I'm thinking I'm fixing to grow up and take a man inside me and I'm moving along in another tarry night through the woods out back of Stanco's Lawn Ornaments and Tombstones and he's got me by the hand saying sweet things like *you little dual-exhaust you, you little road-runner let me rev you up* and I keep on batting at him till we're on a stump at the quarry pond and this is the good part this is the part I knew I'd like, the cuddle beforehand, him knowing I'll say yes and it makes him cuddle real good cause I told him already it's the only way he's getting inside me and I say I got to have a great kiss first and then he can go down there to what he wants and he squares around and puckers and he moves in fast glancing off my nose and sliding along my cheek and he says *oopsie doops sorry there Maisie* and I say *that's okay Elmer* he's so cute being clumsy I know I'll marry him

ROBERT DURAND

Commuter

Beheaded in crash of Staten Island ferry

2003

underneath her earlobe with its wisp of invisible fuzz the cleavage of her toes in her pointiest black stilettos the hollow of her ankle her sacral dimples each holding a tiny shadow as she sleeps in the morning light that slides beneath the shade, unawares she has sloughed off the toga of bedclothes the long indent of her spine bared and those dimples I put the tip of my tongue in one and she stirs, my wife, her shoulders her tall knuckles the lift of her arm the hollow beneath I put my face there and she bats at my ear *I'm not fresh* she says, *it's you* I say, kissing this hidden place, the round forward points of her hips that I palm as she sits upon me, my wife, my Ann, and she will not close her eyes *I want to see you in that moment* she says the knot of her wrist her brow I ruffle her brow with my lower lip the tiny arc of a scar on the back of her hand the mark of a Christmas-tree light the bruises of that childhood long gone and the father dead and the mother too just this scar remains and I turn her hand and I kiss her there and she puts her hands on my cheeks and she draws me to her and presses me down and she kisses me on the top of the head

TYLER **ALKINS**
Civilian truck driver

Beheaded by the Iraqi Al-Tawhid Wal-Jihad (Monotheism and Holy Struggle)

2004

my name is Tyler Alkins my voice sounding far off guttering like the bleeder flames in the refineries outside Houston *my mother's name is Marietta* the red dot on the video camera a drop of blood at the corner of her mouth *my father's name is Ralph* and the old man is upon me grabbing at my shoulder *boy turn around and take this beating now* he says but I wrench my mind to him and me out with shotguns waiting for the doves to break and then he squeezes at my shoulder, but gently, the feathers of a dove fluttering still from the air the kick of the gun shuddering through me and a hand comes upon my shoulder from behind and a voice cries *allahu akbar* and it is just me and my rig driving the interstate hard at night the sodium vapor lamps coming up out of the dark like a sky full of nearby stars *I live in Lubbock, Texas* and our own George is the President and he calls upon all of us and I can drive a truck and my old man grabs my shoulder and I have done something wrong and he says *in the name of Jesus* and a bite at my neck *allahu akbar* and George has prayed to God and he will kick ass and plenty of it and my father cries *take this beating now for your own good*

VASIL **BUKHALOV**

Bulgarian agricultural aid worker

Beheaded by the Iraqi Salafist Brigade of Abu Bakr al-Siddiq
2004

on my tongue the bitter bite of green walnut Baba's face in the lamp light
her hands black from the peeling of the skins the nuts inside white and very
soft, too young yet to be hardened, and I eat another and another until bitter
is sweet to me and the cheese she gives me is soft as well and tastes like the
goat's milk but after it's turned and it tastes also of the stable floor and of
the rutted earth and I make a face I am very young and Baba puts her hand
on mine and she says *eat more and you will find the taste is good* and then
her hand touches my face *you look like your grandfather in this light* and I
have seen a picture on a postcard of Diado and I will look again to see if I
can find my own face and I look into my own son's face and see Diado's eyes
and I make cheese and I grow pears and I give my son a curl of cheese from
my fingertip and he makes a sour face and Baba lays her forearm beneath
the piss-spill of the lamp and she shows me the number there, faint, in blue,
I was in Macedonia because of your grandfather and they took us and this
is all she says and we eat bitter herbs and they taste sweet to me now

ROBERT OLEN **BUTLER**

Writer

Decapitated on the job

2010

heedless words but whispered, they begin as I stand before the guillotine and I am filled with the scent of motor exhaust and wood fire and fish sauce and jasmine in a strange country, a good scent, her hand in mine at last, the city that roars in my dreams is beyond the stucco walls a balcony the Saigon River the rim of the world bleeding from the setting sun and self-righteousness, the guillotine in the museum rises above the cannon barrels and rotor blades and unexploded bombs the blade darkened by the wet air and the voices begin to speak not in my head not in the place where I think but in my ear directly in my fingertips a computer screen before me the clatter of keys like tiny clawed feet running in a wall, come to me little ones nibble from my hands snuggle into my pockets and curl your naked tails in peace like these words already fixed and bound and tucked beneath my arm, half a dozen autographs signed tonight and thanks for buying my book I step into the elevator and I am alone and the air buzzes in silence and I consult the scrap of paper in my pocket to see where I belong and I push the button and down the hall there are voices agitated ardent full of yearning and I lean forward and I stick my head out to listen

PRAISE FOR ROBERT OLEN BUTLER

A Good Scent from a Strange Mountain

'The book has attracted such acclaim not simply because
it is beautifully and powerfully written, but because it convincingly
pulls off an immense imaginative risk... Butler has not only entered
the significant and ever-growing canon of Vietnam-related fiction
(he has long been a member) he has changed its composition forever'
– Claire Messud, *Guardian*

'Deeply affecting ... a brilliant collection of stories about
storytellers whose recited folklore radiates as implicit prayer ...
One of the strongest collections I've read in ages'
– Ann Beattie

'*A Good Scent From a Strange Mountain* is remarkable...
for how beautifully it achieves its daring project
of making the Vietnamese real'
– *New York Times Book Review*

'Butler's achievement is not only to reveal the inner lives of
the Vietnamese, but to show, through their eyes, how the rest
of us appear from an outside perspective'
– *Chicago Tribune*

A Small Hotel

'With mesmerizing detail, Butler excavates layers of memory
and illuminates moments of both tenderness and alienation'
– New Yorker

'Skillful... Absorbing... Wise and painfully realistic...
A novel of ideas, an interrogation of the limitations and uses of language'
– New York Times Book Review

'Intelligent, deeply moving... remarkably written...
A Small Hotel is a masterful story that will remind readers
once again why Robert Olen Butler has been called
the best living American writer'
– Fort Worth Star Telegram

'A sleek, erotic, and suspenseful drama about men
who cannot say the word love and the women they harm...
Butler executes a plot twist of profound proportions in this
gorgeously controlled, unnerving, and beautifully revealing
tale of the consequences of emotional withholding'
– Booklist (starred review)

'A brief, intense portrayal of the collapse of a marriage... This may be
the oldest story in the world, or at least in the monogamous world,
but Butler... seeks to give it new life by anatomizing the feelings
and perceptions of each of the principals... in A Small Hotel he has
performed an unusual and worthy feat. The puzzle may have only
three pieces, but each of these has many facets, and the way
they eventually fit together delivers a surprising charge'
– Washington Post

ALSO BY ROBERT OLEN BUTLER

* Published by No Exit Press

Intercourse

Intercourse

STORIES

ROBERT OLEN BUTLER

NOEXIT2

First published in the UK in 2016
by No Exit Press, an imprint of Oldcastle Books
PO Box 394,
Harpenden, AL5 1XJ, UK

noexit.co.uk
@noexitpress

Some of the stories in this book originally appeared in *Playboy*, *Conjunctions*, *The Kenyon Review*, *The Virginia Quarterly Review*, *Weber*, *New Letters*, *Vestal Review*, and on Nerve.com and NarrativeMagazine.com.

A CIP catalogue record for this book is available from the British Library.

ISBN
978-1-84344-759-7 (print)
978-1-84344-753-5 (epub)
978-1-84344-754-2 (kindle)
978-1-84344-755-9 (pdf)

Design and Typesetting by Elsa Mathern
Printed and bound in Great Britain by Clays Ltd, St Ives plc

The Couples

– What were you thinking?
– When?
– During.
– During.
– Yes. Not what goes where. Thinking deep down.
– About you.
– Liar.
– So what were you thinking?
– About you.

ADAM

7, first man

EVE

7, first woman, his wife

on a patch of earth cleared of thorns and thistles, a little east of Eden,
the first day after the new moon of the fourth month of the eighth year
after Creation

ADAM

the dust of the ground rises around us as we move and clench and thrash, and the Creator's vast dark face fades and the woman grows slick and the dust turns to mud, and in the distance to the west I hear the trees stirring from a sweet breeze, but here the air is still, save for our breath, we are a great wind now ourselves, the two of us, we are rushing across the face of the earth and all that we left behind was good, but behold, naked is good too, and I named the animals one by one, the Creator brought them and I named them, and again I have some naming to do – of these parts of her I am seeing as if for the first time – but that will have to wait, I am a running river now and the names I already named will have to do: her two young fawns, her clam, her ass, which I ride

EVE

I was happy but to tangle the holding parts and the walking parts and lie here quietly in the clean space he has made for us, but he is pawing and fondling and crying out and whimpering and perhaps that is good too, like when he took the apple from me, he was quiet then and he is boisterous now but it is the same: I offer and he takes, and I had nothing to give the Creator and all that He gave was for the man, and a shadow fell on the path and something was there and it came forth hissing prettily and he said *You're not stupid* and he was right and what he gave was sweet in me, but this man is not, he is flailing around and proud of his own little snake

17

ZEUS, IN THE FORM OF A SWAN
982, King of the Gods

LEDA
20, Queen of Sparta

in an inner courtyard in the palace, Sparta, 1215 BC

ZEUS THE SWAN

the swan was a mistake, these creatures who mate with just one, for now that I have her before me I am compelled to explain, though all I have are whoopings and trumpetings and undulant dippings of the head: I am married to my own sister – by Fate, by necessity, you understand – and she has her hair piled high on her head in a polos and she never lets it down and she is murderously jealous and worse, she goes every year to the spring at Kanathos and renews her virginity and I have to start all over again – anyone who desires a virgin is a fool – and you have to understand, my father hated me, he hated all his children, he ate them up at birth, swallowed them whole, and only because my mother gave a swaddled rock in my place did I escape their fate, and growing up I often thought it would have been better just to be eaten, for I spent all my young life dangling from a rope from a tree so that I was neither on the earth nor in the sky nor in the sea and thus invisible to the old man, but it has made the dangling part of my body the most treasured center of my being, you see, and so here I am, the king of the gods, making a fool of myself as a bird just to get under your gown

LEDA

I knew who you were as soon as you flapped down from the moonlit sky and started whooping and trumpeting while my husband snored away inside the palace after emptying himself in me as if I were a fat temple sheep, and now it's you, with your wings quivering and your neck snaking around: if you wanted me so badly why is your breath reeking of barley, you had to turn yourself into a swan, fine, but you have such a passion for me that on your way you had to take time to land in a field somewhere and play the swan eating the crops, and as soon as you're done here you'll be off scudding around on the river with some swan bitch dipping your heads deep under the dark water together sucking at weeds while I'm left with this lesser king and eggs to lay

HELEN

25, Queen of Sparta, wife of Menelaus

PARIS

22, Prince of Troy

in a villa on the island of Cranae in the Laconian Gulf, 1194 BC

PARIS

Cassandra pulled at her hair and proclaimed the fire I will bring to Troy along with my Helen, and at last she is right, my sister the seer, I burned at the first sight of Helen and now I am a raging tall-flamed pine fire at her touch and it will never stop, this hot billowing in me, even as she lies beneath me placid and cool as the snows of Mount Gargarus and her head falls back languidly to the side and her arm rises and her hand curls outward, the long fingers flaring as if to clutch some invisible thing, and I might as well not even be here, for her eyes are the blue of the Aegean and swimming deep inside them, far out of sight, are her goddess thoughts, perhaps of her father Zeus, who waits for her immortal body that one day will lie languidly upon a couch on Olympus when she will belong to the gods, but for now, in spite of her distraction, she is mine

HELEN

he is older, my Menelaus, his arms are strong and he is a king, but too strong, but too much a king: what of the beauty of my face and my neck and my hands and my breasts and my thighs, what of all the heroes of Greece who came to woo me and I chose a man with strong arms who was soon to be a king, but then his vast shadow passed over my face, my body, and I vanished and he would not stand aside, and then a prince came, a young man who chose a gift from between three vying goddesses and he declined the power of a great warrior and he declined the wealth of kings and he chose instead the love of the most beautiful woman in the world, me, who for nine years has lived in a shadow, and so the prince and I have come down from his ship on this island, the spray of salt from the sea still on our eyelids, our lips, our throats, and we have rushed to a private chamber with cicadas singing outside our window and we taste the salt on each other and he is beautiful in face and neck and hands and chest and thighs, but not as beautiful as me

HELEN
35, Princess of Troy

MENELAUS
42, King of Sparta

on board his ship in the Aegean Sea, after retrieving her at the end of the Trojan War, 1184 BC

MENELAUS

this is familiar, after a decade, this is too familiar, I should have just let her go, I should have spared the lives of so many of our warriors, but these are the bodies we men have been given to live in, these are the gods' gifts of sword and shield and knife and fist and teeth and the gifts of strategy and cunning and the gift of bravery to stand before the ferocity of your own imminent death and fight, and so if it had not been for this woman who is beneath me once again that we fought and died, it would have been for something else, in some other place, against some other foe, who, in their own warrior hearts, would have cared as little as we about the reason: it is what we do

HELEN

the gift from the gods rolled heavily in amongst us, towering in the center of our city, a vast horse of pine with a beautiful head, nostrils flared, its mane erect, its flanks glittering with torchlight, and I understand that long before, Paris had become a fool and a coward, shooting arrows from the parapets and pawing at me in our own bed each night as if it were the first time while the heroes of Troy died beyond the walls using their swords, and I understand that my face is still beautiful, even this many years later, even night before last, even lit in the mirror by Troy in flames outside my bedroom window, and I understand the gods gave me the gift of my beauty and the gods gave Paris the gift of the most beautiful woman in the world, but deep within these gifts our own destruction crouched, biding its time

MARY MAGDALENE

24, prostitute

TIBERIUS AURELIUS GAVROS

22, Roman soldier

beneath a fig tree just outside Capernaum on the Sea of Galilee, AD 28

MARY

from a distance, from the shade of a tree where I stood watching him beside
the well, he seemed important, the men around him seemed to wish to shrink
near him, make themselves very small, they were eager for him to speak,
and I thought to wait to find him alone and perhaps he would provide the
pieces of money I need, which this Roman provides now instead, but that
was another woman thinking those things, the same woman beneath this
man now – she does not understand fully yet – even as some other woman,
thinking these new thoughts, hovers a ways apart, up in the branches of this
fig tree, looking off toward the town where I feel him waiting, for at the well
his eyes turned to me, away from the men, I could see his eyes clearly, even
from a distance, and they knew me

TIBERIUS

now that I have killed a man, now that I have at last killed a man – a man
who was crying against Rome and waving a knife in this barren place of
dust and weeds and houses of crude basalt blocks stuffed with mud – now
that the rest of my life has truly begun with the quickness of my hand on my
gladius, its blade going in softly, easily, finding a spot between his ribs, now
that I tremble inside cursing my birth to a father who is a centurion and has
created me for this, now that I tremble for what my hands can so easily do, I
touch this body beneath me with these same hands and beg them remember
this moment when they feel hungry for gentleness, and I wish to thank her,
thank her generosity: though I pay her, it is not enough for what she gives me

CLEOPATRA VII

28, Queen of Egypt

MARCUS ANTONIUS

42, general and member of Rome's ruling triumvirate

on her royal barge in the River Cydnus at Tarsus, AD 41

MARCUS

the sound of flutes and harps and lyres and, in their pausing, the sound of water lapping at the barge and I am an ambitious man and I am a man of battle and my head always has sounds on its horizon – the clanging of swords and the grunting of men and even, to an ear attuned to it, the sucking sound of sword in flesh, and this sound is the same, inside me and out: that soft sucking sound, now beneath me, my mansword and the flesh of a queen, but these other sounds are in me, as well, of the music and of the river in this floating world, where she waited for me tonight amidst a thousand torches, beneath a golden canopy, the queen reclining on her couch draped in an azure peplos fallen off her shoulder to bare her breasts, her hair braided all about her head, she was the very vision of Venus, opening wide for Marcus Antonius, and I am an ambitious man and I can overcome Octavian and rule Rome and perhaps I will, but what higher ambition is there than to fuck a goddess and I might well choose to float on her river forever in peace

CLEOPATRA

how simple it was, how nakedly alluring, me rolled into a carpet like the womb and I rolled out with no sounding of trumpets, no scuffle of subjects going prostrate, and with no perfumes or jewels or silks upon me but I rolled in a thin swaddling of linen as a newborn child onto the floor and the great Julius Caesar rose in surprise from his chair and my breasts had gone bare and my loins as well and I very slowly covered them and spun and folded my legs under me and I lifted my face to him and it began, and Caesar touched me quite gently – unlike this stone-fingered Antonius – and he gave me my throne over my brother, whom he had drowned in the Nile, and my sister, whom he had pursued into exiled refuge in the temple at Ephesus, and he took me to his Rome where he exalted me, and then he died on my behalf on the steps of the Forum, and now with riches and pomp and music it begins again, and though this one touches me roughly, it will do, and the first thing I will ask of him is that he kill my sister

ATTILA

47, Khan of the Huns

ILDICO

17, his twelfth wife

*in his bed in Pannonia, on their wedding night, as he simultaneously
dies from ruptured esophageal varices,* AD 453

ATTILA

a sudden warmth deep in my throat like the bloom on the chest of an enemy as the arrow flies in and I cannot draw a breath and I lift up and try again and again and there is nothing but the old man, the Shaman of Rome, the Papa called Leo, and I am on horseback at the ford of the River Mincius and he comes on foot and I dismount because he wears golden robes and I know he carries invisible arrows, though I can still take his life, my hand moves to the hilt of the Sword of Mars, which came to me long ago as a sign of my greatness, and this man in gold pleads quietly that I do not press on from this place to his Rome to sack it and burn it and he says *Do not think that you deal simply with Valentinian, for my Emperor is not of this world* and I do not understand, but my hand wants to kill him at once and take his golden robe for spoil and I would advance on his city, but then another man appears, assembling himself from the empty air beside the Shaman, and my horse knows to mutter and rear and this man is lank and draped in linen and he has an uneven beard and dark quiet wounds in his side and he wears a crown of thorns and he advances, and though he carries no weapon I begin to tremble, and he says very softly *I am his Emperor* and he stops before me and he angles his head backward and to the side and he offers his naked throat, and I know that if I cut it I am lost

ILDICO

I cannot stop my legs from shaking, my chest from trembling, even with the weight of him on me, and the root of every hair in my head burns from the ceremonial dragging to his bed, and outside, his warriors vibrate their tongues, filling the air with cries like birds of prey come to wait beyond this canopy of white linen, wait in the flicker of pine torch, wait until he is done with me to pick the flesh from my bones, and now he rears like a horse and gasps and gasps, though I can tell he is not finished inside me, and now he falls heavily upon me again and he grows still, and lo, he is suddenly weak, he is gentle suddenly, and a sweet hopeful surging comes into me, for I see there is a side to my fierce new husband that perhaps will let me hold him close, and I put my arms about him

IZUMI SHIKIBU

29, lady of the court, poet

PRINCE ATSUMICHI

31, nobleman of the court, poet, husband of Princess Atsumichi

in Izumi's rooms in the King's North Palace, Kyoto, Japan, 1003

PRINCE ATSUMICHI

she looks at the moon
I see the same moon alone
her poem arrives:
wild geese fly in a night white
with moonlight pure as her heart

IZUMI

what he gives is white
the sea calm then rising up
then coming to shore
the wave rushes and churns thick:
white of the moon, you are dull

LUCREZIA BORGIA

21, daughter of Pope Alexander VI, Rodrigo Borgia

ALFONSO D'ESTE

25, her husband, eldest son of the Duke of Ferrara

in their bridal chamber at the Castello Estense, Ferrara, 1502

LUCREZIA

almost married to Valencia at age eleven, almost married to Naples at twelve, married to Milan at thirteen, a man of twenty-seven years with strong teeth and a limp member, and I wore red velvet trimmed in ermine and woven with gold thread, and when he was useless to the Borgia men – as he was to me – they could have slit his throat and thrown him into the Tiber and I would not have cried, but they simply annulled him and I was married at seventeen to Naples, to Alfonso of Bisceglie, who was seventeen, and we were one in mind and body as well as years and his skin was smooth as Travertine marble and I wore black velvet and I was a night sky of rubies and diamonds and I wore a girdle of pearls and a diadem of chased gold, and when he was useless to the Borgia men – though I loved him desperately still – my brother had him stabbed and beaten and then my brother strangled him to death with his own hands, and today I wore a gown of gold with purple satin stripes and sleeves of ermine and a cloak of ermine and I give my body now to Ferrara and he is accustomed to whores and he is accustomed to artillery but he has taken me away from Rome at last, far away, far from Rome at last, and at last I no longer have to look at the face of my father, the face of Christ's Church on earth, for my father took my body to himself when I was eight and in the dark he whispered *You will always be married to me*

ALFONSO

it is whispered in certain places that she poisoned the last one, some boy, and it is whispered she nightly fucks her father on the altar of St. Peter and it is whispered she had his bastard son, a creature with horns and a cloven hoof they had to burn at the stake before the sunset of its first day, but my father says she is a crucial alliance with Rome and she is the city of Cento and the city of Pieve and the harbor of Cesenatico and she is a dowry of a hundred thousand ducats and for these things she is not a murderer and she is not a slut to her father, and I did not truly know what she was until I rode out to her procession a day early and caught her just arrived for the night at Castel Bentivoglio and she came to me in the courtyard brushing the road dust from her riding dress and her golden hair was falling about her shoulders and she surely was unhappy at my seeing her for the first time like this and she lifted her long face to me and her pale blue eyes fixed on me and she smiled a smile like the muzzle flash of a cannon and I took her hand and bent low to kiss it and she whispered *I am your wife* and I knew that she was

HENRY VIII
44, King of England

ANNE BOLEYN
34, Queen of England

at the house of Sir William Sandys near Basingstoke, England,
OCTOBER 1535

HENRY

he conjures himself corporeal from the very air: imperious dark eyes and cropped auburn hair and a small mouth shaping kisses and pouts and commands and his shoulders are broad and his limbs are long and his fingertips flare above the vast dark ocean on one side and the wide cold sea on the other and he steps forward with first one foot upon the cliffs of Cornwall and then the other upon Dover and he bestrides the land and he looks out to the wide world beyond, my son, my sweet son, and as I am England now, he will be England then, and by the prickish essence I give yet again to this woman, I will be England once more. Or else

ANNE

I alone made England's alliance with France and I lifted the worldly evils of the papacy from our peoples' religious life and I bestowed all the wisdom of Cromwell upon the king and I established the right of a commoner to become a noble by his own thoughts and deeds and I gave more alms to the poor of the land than any highborn in history, and it all comes to this: a bejeweled codpiece falls and from a slash in a pair of breeches comes a too-small prick attached to a fat and distracted man and if its fluids do not blend with mine such to create a boy, I will sure be cast aside, or worse, and all that I am, all that I ever can be, is my cunt

WILLIAM SHAKESPEARE
29, poet and playwright

HENRY WRIOTHESLEY
THIRD EARL OF SOUTHAMPTON
20, courtier and literary patron

in Shakespeare's rooms in St. Helen's Bishopsgate, London, 1593

WILLIAM

proud Nature humbled by the work of its own hand: his azure eye, his
auburn tress, the chest it hangs on white as the sun can seem when veiled
in silken cloud, his silken doublet white as cloud cast off to bare the fire
beneath, and if his heart be sun and his chest be sky then his eye be heaven
and his earth below be forested lush around a great high oak that stands
stripped clean of limbs from lightning strike: I give my limbs to this land
and touch his beating heart and burn, and yet he is night as well as day, a
well as well as tree, a well dug deep and dark and I send my vessel down: he
is, in flesh, the world inconsonant made one: my young man, my dark lady

HENRY

I soon will lie alone and he will cross the room and sit at his table and once
again he will take up his goose quill and find it blunt and take up his knife
and bend and squint and turn slightly to the light from the window and
begin his sweet circumcision, playing at the tip with the blade, making it less
blunt, then sharp, then sharper still, and he will pause and touch the tip to
his tongue and he will pull the ink pot nearer to him and dip the pen, dip it
deep, the tip growing wet and dark, and he will withdraw and let it drip and
drip till it stops, and then he will bend to his paper and his words will come
and the tiny scratch of his quill will shudder its way up my thighs and I am
pen and I am ink and I am his words

COTTON MATHER

56, clergyman and author

LYDIA LEE MATHER

45, his third wife

in their home in Boston, 1719

COTTON

O Heavenly Father, please let this madness lift from her, my sweet Consort, my temporal delight, my Wife, for I know she is merely mad, I acknowledge the errors of my youth when I spoke and wrote to condone the hunt for witches in Salem, the nineteen hanged and the four who died awaiting the gallows and the one pressed to death by stones all hover about my soul and, to their credit, mercifully hold their tongues, but I feel them there and I acknowledge my sins against them for they were at worst mad, and if one or two were what was feared, then it would have been better that those go free than that the innocently deranged, Your children in need, be persecuted, and You are teaching me still, O stern and loving Father: she hissed and she wailed and she threw an ink pot and she ripped my sermon and she stood trembling in the kitchen and cursed me and cursed the hearth and cursed the broom and cursed the veal and the butter and the pickled barberries and yet abruptly these paroxysms ended, as they always do, and then she humbled her body before me in tender entreaties and ardent praises and sweet pleadings for us to enact the meek and abject yielding that is her proper place in the world that You have created, and I beg You, O Heavenly Father, to forgive these worldly acts we presently perform and to transform them into a healing of her affliction

LYDIA

O pudding, O pudding for my husband, O pudding I dance you, my pudding, I sing you, my pudding, for you are my life, my pudding of hog's liver, my Lord and husband's favorite, I will take a nice fat liver and I will work it in my hands for a time and I will parboil it and I will shred it small, very small, so it will soften sweetly and it will give forth its juices, and I will beat the pieces very fine in a mortar and mix them in my earthen pot with the thickest and sweetest cream and I will strain it and into the liver I will put six yolks of eggs and two whites of eggs and the grated crumbs of a penny whiteloaf and then currants and dates and cloves and mace and coarse-grain sugar and saffron and salt and an excellent swine suet, but before the boiling and before the laying of it all on the iron grid over the coals for broiling, when, my sweet pudding, you are still raw and redolent of organ and spices and blood, I will add a tittle of wormwood and a minim of henbane and the eye of a freshly killed newt

WOLFGANG AMADEUS MOZART
31, composer

NANCY STORACE
21, soprano

in her rooms at the Hotel Belvedere in Vienna, after the premiere of his aria "Ch'io mi scordi di te," written for her, on the eve of her permanent departure to her home country of England, FEBRUARY 23, 1787

WOLFGANG

I leap onto her lap and into her arms and I am six years old and she is the Empress and I am a genius I am a miracle the fingers of my left hand are still tingling from the violin strings and they find first the rope of pearls along her waist and then the embedded diamonds upon her stomacher and the ruffle along her bodice and at last ever so delicately the flesh of her in the treble cleft of breasts and chest and as my hand moves I kiss her throat a long run of demisemiquaver kisses and I am but a little boy, she thinks, as she lifts my offending hand and kisses its palm and perhaps I am but I am a genius and her flesh smells of musk and upon it are the smells of orange blossom and sandalwood and rose and she laughs a trilling laugh and holds me close and later, beyond her sight and the Emperor's, I stand beside Maria Antonia Josefa Johanna von Habsburg-Lothringen their daughter and her eyes are an arpeggio of gray and blue and her lower lip is pouting all the time and we have counted it out that she is but eighty-six days older than me and I put my hand in hers and I begin to finger the Bach D-Minor Chaconne in her palm and she angles her head a little in my direction *I will marry you* I say but I did not and now my fingers fly upon soprano-flesh encoring my farewell to Nancy this night: I play the pianoforte upon her, modulating from the G minor of the recitative to the E-flat major of the aria, and though she fills the room with the trilling of her laughter I can hear her singing

NANCY

I have filled my mouth with him, with his music, and I sing him even now in my head where my voice does not have to keep up, where I do not have to sing actual words, it is all *nota e parola*, every note a sound, and so I cling with an infant's babble to his back and we rise up and float out the window and we fly, as only composers can fly, on pure senses, just the sound itself, no words at all, no meanings, and I cling to him and his bones are fragile as a bird's and his heart beats fast as a bird's and we fly above Vienna and out into the mountains and I look higher into the night sky and my mind slows and the lights burn at the edge of the stage and I lift my face toward the Emperor in his gilded box and I sing actual words *Stelle barbare, stelle spietate* and I sing this now to the sky outside our window *Oh brutal stars, oh pitiless stars* in the morning I will leave this tiny man with the bad skin and his ravening restlessness and whose genius presently animates his hands upon me: your music is perfect, my little Wolfgangerl, but for this, there are too many notes

LOUIS XVI

23, King of France

MARIA ANTONIA JOSEFA JOHANNA VON HABSBURG-LOTHRINGEN

KNOWN IN FRANCE AS MARIE ANTOINETTE

21, Queen of France

for the first time, on the eve of their seventh wedding anniversary, in the royal bedroom at Versailles, MAY 15, 1777

LOUIS

she doesn't like me smelling of coal fire from my forge where I have just repaired a beautiful old Beddington lock and she narrows her little pig eyes at me and pouts out even farther her Habsburg lower lip and her hair is poufed up high and appears to have tiny birds living in it along with their nest and parts of a tree, and her brother has arrived from Austria and is about to insult me, and if I were my father, if I actually wanted to be what I am, I would have this man's head cut off with a blunt ax after he walks me through the grounds of the Trianon and asks if my member is working properly, and now I must try to understand that this matter is about a key and a lock: her warded lock, full of hidden obstructions, cylinders and flat metal plates with tiny separations that must all be entered at precise angles and all at once, and my key must somehow fit, and perhaps it is true that the future of France depends on this thing I am now doing but I would much prefer to put my member in the forge until it is yellow-hot from the flame and then pound it on an anvil with a hammer

MARIE

I turn my face away and angle my head down and against my shoulder and I try to smell myself and not the royal blacksmith who has somehow found his way to my bed in place of the king who vanished long ago, and I smell of jasmine and iris and orange blossom and tuberose and cedar and I am but a little girl and my mother the queen's own fingertip draws a cool line of scent behind my ear and now she and I are listening to a little boy playing his violin and even as his one hand moves quickly on the neck of his instrument and the other draws the bow slowly he lifts his eyes to me and they are blue-gray just like mine and now we are standing apart and I feel his hand slip into mine and he begins to touch me there: his fingers run about my palm as if I were his violin and he begins to hum a sweet soft tune so that only I can hear and I know he loves me and I think to lean over and kiss him but my mother looks my way from across the room and lifts her hand to call me to her and I do not kiss him, but now yes, but now yes, I turn my face and I lean close and I kiss my Wolfgang Amadeus on the cheek and I whisper *Marry me*

THOMAS JEFFERSON

45, U.S. Ambassador to France

SALLY HEMINGS

16, slave, half-sister to Jefferson's dead wife

at his residence in the Hôtel de Langeac, Paris, 1788

THOMAS

the last eight miles to my hilltop on horseback in deep snow, Patty throwing
her head back to laugh, her breath pluming into the moonlight *How difficult
it is to come home with you, Mr. Jefferson* and then the doorway is drifted
high with the snow and I lift her into my arms to carry her through and the
servants are asleep and the fires are out and we are home at last and I find
a Château Latour and I start a fire and we drink and she turns her face to
me *My husband* she says and there in our bedroom on our wedding night
the firelight isn't enough to keep the night's darkness from tainting her face,
like this face now, Sally's, her very blood shared with Patty, but her face
darkened from within, as if through memory, as if by death, as if by my six-
year grief, and Patty throws her head back at the run of her hands on the
keys and I finger my strings lightly, the Bach sonata carrying us both and I
am wooing still and she will say yes and we will marry and she will die, and
I look into these eyes now and now and they are dark, Patty's hazel charred
into deep blackness, but the shape of them is the same and I hear the Bach
and I run now inside like Patty's hands running on her harpsichord I run
and I run and I pursue my happiness

SALLY

so easy to come to this at last: he is playing his violin and it is very sad, the
music, and I stand for a long while quiet in the doorway, behind him, his
shoulders hunched forward a little, his hair – I have enough of the blood
of my father and my mama's father in me that I can blush in this color of
his hair – he bears my blush, which I see on my cheeks in the mirror with
the eagle near the parlor door when I turn my face at his passing – his hair
catches the light from the fireplace and he draws his bow back and forth
on his violin, his elbow rising and falling – and I move to him and he stops
playing, he knows I am behind him, and he knows how fast my heart is
beating, and he ceases playing and he turns to me and his eyes are so sad and
I will never as long as I live know how I come to lift my hand and put it on
my master's face but I do and I am happy

NAPOLÉON BONAPARTE

26, general in command of the French "Army of Italy"

JOSÉPHINE DE BEAUHARNAIS

33, his wife

FORTUNÉ

4, pug, her dog

at the Palazzo Serbelloni, Milan, in the midst of his invasion of Italy, their third night together in the 129 days of their marriage, JULY 13, 1796

JOSÉPHINE

O my darling my darling, in bed again with you my darling, we shall be in bed again soon, even as we fucked our way from Paris to Milan, O my lieutenant, my hussar, my sweet Hippolyte, from inn to inn and also from riverbank to meadow and even, with sublime alacrity, in the carriage while the entourage pissed behind trees, the new France does not understand its own military ranks: attend to the true insignia, ye Directors of the Republic, this lieutenant is far above this general and it is signified by neither gorget nor epaules but by the length of their swords, though, my darling Hippolyte, I'm afraid you must share my love, share my bed, for sometimes it is necessary that love gently separate itself in two, and my other love breathes heavily now and I listen to him with sweet attention: he sat until a few moments ago at the foot of the bed watching, my sweet Fortuné, and I hear him still

NAPOLÉON

consider the musket, our infantry's beloved Charleville, consider the musket ball and its speed from the muzzle, slow, in truth, climbing quickly and falling quickly, as well, aim carefully, my men, at the head from two hundred meters, at the waist from a hundred, at the knees from fifty, so for my wife, who took her blatant neglectful time joining her triumphant husband, I ponder a near shot, aiming at her shins and plugging her in her womanhood, and as for this wretched animal she insists on having in our bed, I will put the muzzle in its mouth so there is no doubt, but now, but wait, ah my wife, my ravishing Joséphine, she banishes these thoughts at once by touching the back of my thigh, clasping me there with her befurred womanhood: and yet how can that be, for she is below me

FORTUNÉ

big dog on my doggie and I missed her signifying or I'd've been there first, but itchy itchy now and I niggle my claw into my side and that's very good, and I could just keep doing this, I suppose, till my doggie is done with the big stinky slick dog, niggle niggle at my side, but now the itchy is gone and I stop, a little regretful, for that was a nice itchy-niggly, and my tongue is cool, flopping in the air, and there's something gathering in my nose and another itchy begins down in my snozzle, and I wonder if I need to do some licking there, but no, snozzle has its own uppity uppity ideas now, and my doggie is occupied but, surprisingly, since it's sickly slick, there's suddenly a certain je ne sais quoi about the big dog, and I hop on

BENJAMIN
23, field slave

HANNAH
17, house slave

in his slave quarters, Adams County, Mississippi, 1855

BENJAMIN

the bells going now in the middle of the night and the dogs' barking getting farther off toward the river and they say Jacob done run off and I seed him take the bullwhip today and I seed his face and I knowed he was up to running at last and the whip fire on my own back make me hold her on our sides and she is here, from the house she all the sudden here, and Jacob done give us this moment, in all the fuss she come to me and for God's sake she be soft along my thighs and on my belly and she be soft against my chest and she be soft upon my manhood and she be putting her soft mouth on mine and I am about to weep like the little nigger boy I used to be cause this is all so sweet and soft

HANNAH

hold tight my Ben my Ben for the first time my Ben my Ben: you go ahead make a sound now please, you don't have to do quiet, there be plenty of uproar outside so you make a sound that can take Master's voice away from my head *Come here girl come here* and it's even bright morning sun and it's even his own parlor and it's even his wife's stuffed couch and it's her antimacassar I am clutching hard crumpling in the palm of my hand while he be doing that thing and I be looking off to the sun out the window and I wants to keep looking till I can go blind but I look away cause I think of that man I seed out the window yesterday who sees me and I make it in my head he be mine someday and I want to have eyes to see him, and now there ain't no sun and there be just pine board and a corn-shuck mattress and he doing close upon me and now he do make a sound, a small one, something like the sound you make holding back your voice when you is whipped, but it's okay, my Ben, that sound'll do

JOHN WILKES BOOTH
24, actor

CATHERINE WINSLOW
26, actress

in his rooms at the National Hotel, Washington, DC, after the opening of his production of Richard III, *which was attended by President and Mrs. Abraham Lincoln,* APRIL 11, 1863

JOHN

you dare to watch even this, I look over my shoulder and there you are,
sitting across the room, spindleleg crossed over spindleleg, cheeks sunk
deep, sucked dry, as you are, of the last dewdrop trace of humanity, and
you watch me in this bed even as you watched me tonight from your box:
be gone, tyrant, be gone, don't you understand when I, as the villainous
Richard, crawled on my belly like a snake on Bosworth Field, it was you
I portrayed, it was you in my mind and in my body, and I regret this for
Richard's sake, regret that I sensed you there watching and, in doing so,
envenomed my Richard into a creature far more vile than he was – what
were his sins compared to yours? your hobnailed boot pressed on the throat
of a nascent nation, and even in my own Maryland, unconfederated still,
you jail us without warrant, intercept our mail, persecute us for speaking
our minds – and I grind now at Kate, my sweet Kate, my long-limbed Kate,
she is Juliet above, on a balcony, combing her hair *She speaks yet she says
nothing, what of that? her eye discourses, I will answer it* and I do, thrust by
thrust, thrust by deep thrust, as deep as I would plunge a knife into a chest
or fire a bullet into a brain, even as you clear your throat across the room

CATHERINE

I saw what you thought no one saw, in your delicacy, the poor fool of a local
actor in Chattanooga taken on at the last moment to play Montague and not
merely forgetting his lines with you but swirling them up in some perverse
new order which only made you look bad to a full house, and in the wings
you put your arm around the man and I drew near, behind you, to hear you
say, quite softly *Don't worry, my friend, you'll do better tomorrow* and the
man wept on your shoulder, grateful, I'm sure, that you had not murdered
him, which actors of only half your fame would be inclined to do, my sweet
Wilkes, and oh how your Romeo tossed me around in passion, more Walt
Whitman than William Shakespeare, my wild Wilkes, and always the grand
grabbing and lifting and swooping would end with some grace note of your
gentleness, a fingertip trailing across my wrist, the softest touch of your lips,
a low word or two below your breath, that secret tender heart of yours: *My
sweet Kate I see you clearly* and you do, and though you drive deep into me
now such as to make my teeth rattle, I see your gentle eyes flash as I have not
seen them before, flash with a dark loving fire for me

ABRAHAM LINCOLN
54, President of the United States

MARY TODD LINCOLN
44, First Lady

in their bedroom on the second floor of the White House, Washington, DC, after attending the opening night of Richard III, starring John Wilkes Booth, APRIL 11, 1863

ABRAHAM

she rail-split my log long ago, the products of which were dispatched to erect a fence in some far land and leaving nothing erectable behind, but tonight my Mary wants this again after such a long while and what she needs is far above my poor power to add or detract, so I try to see her once more across the dance floor at the General Assembly ball, and her cousin Major Stuart has her by the elbow and is guiding her my way and her eyes are certainly blue, even from a distance, and her chestnut ringlets of hair quake above a great expanse of an exposed bosom that has been much admired all around already, I am fully aware, and she has not yet shrieked at me, indeed, in that moment as she draws near, has not yet spoken a single word to her future husband, though now, in this bed, she will soon speak at my slowness to respond, shriek, in fact, so let us strive on to finish the work we are in, and I do, I turn to look in another direction, my leg crossed, my hands on the arms of my chair, I look to the bright glow of the stage below me, just a few hours ago, and his face turns up and his eyes are as black as a cougar's come upon on a moonless night, and like the cougar's they burn, and if a cougar can purr, which being a cat, surely it can, this is its sound, the voice of this man before me: *Grim-visaged war hath smoothed his wrinkled front, and now, instead of mounting barbed steeds to fright the souls of fearful adversaries, he capers nimbly in a lady's chamber to the lascivious pleasing of a lute:* and his *lascivious pleasing* sighs its sibilance through my loins, even now, and I stir

MARY

when Richard III began to crawl on his belly like a snake crying for a horse in vain, I knew the President would die, and soon, but I am a brave woman and so I did not throw myself headfirst from the box, I went on instead with my hands folded in my lap, with my eyes holding steady on this actor, who was ludicrously beautiful as the ugly king, and I waited for this house and this bed before I would myself cry out, from my fear, but now the cries do not come and all I want is this man once more inside me, a last time inside me, and would that tonight's beautiful actor could play this ugly king, but Abe will do, Abe will have to do, Abe I suppose, is necessary in this surprising desire, except Abe will not do, he is slack and slow and so there is nothing to be done about the knife or the bullet or the bomb, there is nothing to do about this man's distaste for me, and words begin to boil up in my bosom and I try to see him standing beside me in the parlor of my sister's house and

Reverend Dresser is before us in canonical white and his brow is furrowed with God's serious purpose and Abe is absolutely still, not a twitch, the ring, I know, in his hand, engraved Love Is Eternal, and I am in white muslin and it's raining outside, raining hard, and I let the back of my hand touch his, and suddenly now he has caught up and there is a touch, now and now, and he is my husband and he is the President and we both shall soon die

MARTHA JANE "CALAMITY JANE" CANARY

24, frontierswoman

JAMES BUTLER "WILD BILL" HICKOK

39, gambler and gunfighter

in a back room at E. A. Swearingen's Cricket Saloon, JULY 31, 1876

JANE

he's been losing at poker and drinking himself almost to blindness but not quite, I got him away first and I know he can still see out of those pale blue eyes and it's me he's seeing and I reined in my own jag so I could do this and remember it later, if anything's been worth doing in my life it's Wild Bill and me in this bed right now and it's been brewing since Fort Laramie and the trail to the Black Hills where he could see firsthand how I could do with a team of mules – bullwhacking better than any man – and I killed a coyote from a hundred yards with an 1860 Colt Army pistol while all the men were missing with rifles and he could see this, my Bill, he could see with his own eyes, and even though it finally took a goddamn dress and a goddamn bath and me hanging on his arm like a white-slave girl afraid for her life, he's mine now and he's looking me straight and true in the eyes while I go at him and I can hardly see him for my own goddamn girl's tears because I know this is never going to happen again

BILL

I think I'm dead I think I'm dead and I can smell the flames of perdition already and I'm getting a little hot around the edges and it's begun, but they got to bury me first and some damn fool is acting like she don't even know how to lay a man into his coffin, give me back my goddamn clothes you ain't gonna bury me in the raw and they don't stuff you with anything in Deadwood but lead so just put my duds back on and leave me alone cause I'm a goner and I'm about to start weeping like a girl for some thing or other but what goddamn good was it all anyway, I think I'll just weep for my pair of sweet Colt 1851 Navy thirty-sixes with that cool slick ivory on my palms and the hammers cocked at the tips of my thumbs and then them barking away straight and true and no man could stand fair and square before me like that and live, and I wonder how they got me, probably from behind

WALT WHITMAN

64, poet

OSCAR WILDE

28, poet and playwright

*in Whitman's bedroom in his brother's house on Stevens Street
in Camden, New Jersey, 1883*

WALT

for this poet I sing, for this large boy, who cast off black velvet coat, cast off pink cravat, cast off white silk shirt, cast off salmon-colored stockings – O thou legs of many legs! not cast off the stockings so much as carefully peeled each and shook it out and draped it so as not to make it run – and he presents eyes now gray now pale blue, jaw pendulous, lips tumescent, fingers long and fondling, and he is not farmer, not ship joiner, not sawyer, not mule skinner, not coal miner or fireman or hog reeve or hawker or lamplighter – perhaps lamplighter, with my lamp only, whose wick he puts to flame – not butcher or cobbler or cook but poet but young but beautiful, my beard is white my skin is coarse my one arm and one leg are weak still, from their stoppage long ago, and they will stop again soon, leg and arm and belly and man-root and heart and mouth, but for now I sing

OSCAR

your body is not electric, my captain, it is not even a steam engine, it is a wood fire in an open field – I will say on Hampstead Heath, it is bad enough to think of the outdoors, so I will at least imagine your embers within the London city limits – but this room of yours, my dearest Walt, if only books and newspapers and foolscap were made of porcelain and pewter and cloisonné you would still have a distressing jumble of an antique shop but at least one could take a breath and handle an object or two, though do not mistake me, dear old man, I am not ungrateful as I touch you – every pubic inch of space is a miracle – we share so much, for out in the world they speak and write of us viciously, but contempt breeds familiarity and how sad it would be to make such grand gestures as we do make and not have the wide world to witness them, though this private gesture is, for the moment, the grandest of all, my sweet barbarian, your beard smells not of trees but of book paper and we are one: I sound my nuanced yip in the parlors of the world

SIGMUND FREUD
42, psychiatrist

MINNA BERNAYS
33, his sister-in-law

in room 11 at the Schweizerhaus, Maloja, in the Swiss Alps, before sunrise, AUGUST 14, 1898

SIGMUND

only a few minutes ago in a dream I flew out this window and into the dark of the night and I was high above the rooftops of Maloja and before me I could see one isolated mountain rising from the Alps, tall and white in the moonlight, and I flew toward it faster and faster and then I was upon it, clinging to the merest bits of rock on its vast side, and above somewhere was a bird's nest and I had to go there, I began to climb the mountain and above me I could hear the mother bird in the nest – the loving mama bird – and I knew she was feeding two of her children – two female birds – and I was driven to climb faster and faster – I had to find the mother bird – I realized she would die unless I could find her quickly and put my hand upon her – and I climbed even faster, breathlessly, and at last I reached a ledge and I lifted my head and in front of me was the nest, wide and deep, and sitting inside were three birds – three plump, gray-feathered, long-beaked female birds – and they turned their heads to look at me and, as young birds of a certain age often are, the two girlchicks were indistinguishable from the mother bird – all three birds were identical and I had no way to sort them out, but I had to reach in and touch the mother in her nest or she would die: I looked at the three birds, the three birds looked at me, and then suddenly it was all right, suddenly it didn't matter, any of them would do: so here I am fucking my mother

MINNA

I was very small and the room was very quiet for he had stopped breathing, my Papa, and then the room was full of my mother's sobbing, but what I noticed most was the smell of cigar smoke, the room was hazy with smoke, he'd had a last smoke before dying, he'd drawn into himself the smoke that I later understood helped kill him and then he'd breathed it back into the room and it hung in the air all about me, the smoke from his ravaged lungs hung all around and I knew he'd left me, I knew Papa had left me, and Ignaz my betrothed came home from Oxford and he lay in his room coughing and bleeding from the lungs and I stood in the doorway and he waved me away, perhaps for my sake, and he coughed and coughed again and then he left me also, and even when he is naked, Sigmund smells like cigars and he coughs a nasty rattling cough, but I know how I have done this, I know why I can tolerate loving him: because when he leaves, it won't be me he's leaving, it'll just be my sister

LIZZIE ANDREW BORDEN

44, murderer, acquitted in 1892

NANCE O'NEIL

30, actress

in O'Neil's home, Brindley Farm, Tyngsboro, Massachusetts, 1904

LIZZIE

her hands the hands of Lady Macbeth that first time I saw her at the Colonial in Boston, she stands in a bright spot of light, her crimson hands flaring delicately before her, her eyes aflame at the only man in her world because he is a coward, and her vast, trilling voice fills me *A little water clears us of this deed* and I stand for a long while before him as he sleeps in the sitting room on the mohair sofa in his morning coat, his feet on the floor, and he is snoring, this man whose name I bear, whose touch I bear, my Papa, and the stepmother is finished already, upstairs, and the short-handled ax is light in my hand and I wait upon myself to decide: he gave away our farm in Swansea to the dead cow upstairs and he gave away the house on Fourth Street to her sister, and though to do all that would never have occurred to him on his own, he could not resist, he is a coward, and now Lady Macbeth pulls me close: a little of her wetness clears me of this deed

NANCE

from a poisonous heaven I want nothing to do with or from a hell in what may secretly be a just universe, look upon your daughter now, Father, look upon my nakedness and Lizzie Borden's and pound your chest in shame as you did with me trapped in the middle of a packed pew where you placed me so you could cry out my evil to heaven and the congregation *She goes off to a life in the theater and thereafter to an eternity in hell* and I tried once more with you, my bag was packed and I was looking beautiful – I could see myself in the foyer mirror and I trembled at myself and wanted you to tremble too – and you cried *Get thee behind me* but Lizzie would know what to do with you, Father, she would know: your hands are as hard as ax heads, Lizzie, your hands are as hot as blood, your hands have spots upon them, sweet Lizzie, just rub them clean on me

JAMES JOYCE
24, writer

NORA BARNACLE
22, his wife

in their apartment on the Via Giovanni Boccaccio, Trieste, MAY 23, 1906

JAMES

in the midst she's suddenly ghosteyed and boyfingered and she's gone away from me: who's that knocking at my door? a semen-sappy boy soprano singing *It's only me from over the sea, I'm Barnacle's Mike the sailor* and in he comes from his grave and he's ready to rollick her all over and he's barely had a chance to elbow Jim to the side in his own bed when I am moved to cry *Who the lungbloody hell is knocking up my door this time?* to which, in gas-worky tenor, comes *It's only me from over the sea, I'm Barnacle's Mike the sailor* and sailor Mike the First, otherwise known as her girlhoodlove Saint Michael the Typhoided, having horned in, now horns out, and we slide away together side-by-hornied-side and press against the wall and sailor Mike the Second, otherwise known as her girlhoodlove Saint Michael the Consumptive, enters in from his grave and he sits beside us and we are trinitized before the flail of her and I implore them both to neither Nora burrower nor a Nora bender be, but I am the Madeflesh here and I've got God and the Holy Ghost on either side of me and how do I ever find frigging peace without having to die first

NORA

I can hear his voice clear as can be and he's singing and it's August hot all around and it's dark but I am sitting still in my seat at the Antient Concert Rooms and he's in the bright lights onstage and John McCormack the Great is upcoming to sing but he sings first, my Jim, and it's the Croppy Boy confessing to a priest that he's going to fight for Ireland and the priest is a yeoman captain in disguise who jails him and murders him and I listen and I play the part of the croppy boy though it's me in my girl body and it's Jim that's hiding in priest's clothes and not knowing it's him I confess my lust for him since I'm after slipping my hands down his trousers when early we went walking and Jimmy was getting all jammy in my fingers and he sings so sweet so much sweeter than anyone could possibly sing even John McCormack and I'm still confessing to Father James and then he throws off his vestments and he jimmies me open and I'm trying to sit still in my seat his voice is so sweet and in my head he jims me full to bursting and though the concert room is deep summer hot my body shivers cold with joy as if there was snow falling all around

PABLO PICASSO
24, artist

FERNANDE OLIVIER
25, model

on the forest floor on the slopes of Pedraforca in Catalonia, Spain,
JULY 1906

PABLO

the chase through the trees her naked body flashing in sunlight her skin Yellow Ochre lightened only a little, a stand of downy oaks their foreground barks Cobalt Black cut and cut by Lead White, the trunks going darker as they recede into the shadows all around, the shadows black from Ultramarine and Rose Madder and a little Viridian to take out the purple, a black that has not forgotten the sunlight but where the Iberian wolves can live, and she is laughing and I catch her up and we fall and she rolls away, her body growing dark from the forest floor and my palette turns simple: it is the carbon black of charred bones of a cave-mouth fire and the flat yellows and browns and reds of the earth itself mixed with animal fat and I paint her on rock like an ancient beast with a thin stroke of black going into her to bring her down and there is a rushing in me and my hands are restless my hands are ravenous they move and with the fire-blackened stump of a wood shard I bring a wolf from the forest and it rages into her and rips her body apart beneath me and I paint in her blood, heavy and hard, impasto layer on layer, the Alizarin Crimson pure, my brush slashing like the teeth of the beast

FERNANDE

in the first moments I was wet through with an August rain and he blocked my way into the Bateau-Lavoir though it seemed I could just rush over him he was such a small thing and he had a wet kitten tucked into the crook of his arm and I was living where I was living having escaped the fists of a father and a shop-clerk husband and then a sculptor and yet I could be alone in this strange warren of artists and I could be naked with them and they would be across the room and I could just sit and hold very still and this was a small obstacle, this man, until the few moments after the first moments when I looked into his eyes and no layer-after-layer of Cobalt Black could put the darkness of his eyes on canvas and yet – and yet – he held up this kitten mewing in his hands and he said in terrible French that he was its savior and I knew he was and I began to purr

GERTRUDE STEIN
36, writer

ALICE B. TOKLAS
33, her companion

in their apartment at 27 rue de Fleurus, Paris, 1910

GERTRUDE

I touch her black wisp of a mustache the bottom edge of her black mustache just above her lip, certainly it is her mustache certainly it is hers the black mustache is hers certainly I touch her wisp of a mustache certainly with my fingertip along her lip certainly it is her lip certainly I touch above her lip I draw my fingertip along her black mustache above her lip I draw with my fingertip along her mustache from left mustache to middle indent along her mustache to right mustache and to middle indent and to left I draw my fingertip along her black wisp of a mustache: a melody, a shadow, an antimacassar, a white stain is wet weather is wet whether or not my fingertip draws a line that my fingertip draws along her mustache: this is this, this is certainly this mustache: her mustache is her mustache is her mustache

ALICE

only done a few minutes ago typing upon her large novel on the big black Smith Premier in the atelier from the sheets of foolscap she wrote in the night that fall beside the desk as I type like leaves from a white tree and my fingers are slim and quick and they can do this thing for her whose hands are heavy with man muscle and whose fingers are plump and not suited to this work and for her also I sat with Madame Matisse this morning and spoke of the weather and the fashions and the vegetables while the husband spoke of genius with my Lovey in another room and I am happy to do this for her whenever a genius shows up with his woman, Madame Braque and Madame Gris and Picasso's Fernande and all the rest, and in the other room my Lovey is the plumpest manmuscled genius of any of them and when she touches me she is more man than woman the most man of any woman the most woman the most womanman the most woman who is a man who is a woman and she is both and both is she and both is so much better

VICTOR DE SATODE PEÑASCO Y CASTELLANA

18, of independent means from Madrid

MARIA JOSEFA PEREDEZE SOTO Y VALLEJO PEÑASCO Y CASTELLANA

17, his newly wed wife

in their first-class cabin, C-65, on the RMS Titanic, near midnight, APRIL 14, 1912

VICTOR

Señor John Jacob Astor smiled at me, he came into the first-class dining saloon from the private party in the à la carte restaurant and it was time for cigars and he was speaking to an older man whose name I did not know and then he looked across at me and then at my wife and then back to me and he smiled, one gentleman to another, one man to another, the two men with the most beautiful wives on the ship – his as young as mine, which made the smile even better, wiping away the years between us, we were simply two men who know what this sweetness is – and tomorrow I will stay for the cigars and I will approach him and we will smile and we will smoke a Fernández Garcia together, man to man, but tonight it is not man to man, I am married to the most beautiful woman on this great ship and I carried her to the room so she would know she is mine forever as her father promised, and now we are together and I feel her tremble at my touch and as if by magic the whole room trembles with her

MARIA

at the bottom landing of the Grand Staircase he swept me into his arms without a word and we looked each other in the eyes – we had seen each other's faces for such a little time – our true faces and not just photographs, not just the faces we put on sitting twice in my parents' parlor – and I did not know Victor de Satode Peñasco y Castellana to be a man who would lift me as easily as a goose-down pillow and to hold me close, but he is such a man, and he began to climb and I threw my head back into the nighttime sunlight of electric lights and we climbed and a bronze cherub appeared holding a lamp and this was our floor, only one above the dining room, and I whispered *Higher* and he carried me up to another landing and another until all I could see were the lights in the vast dome right above me and when we reached the top of the staircase I realized that we are married also for love, and I am breathless now with him upon me and all at once I tremble, but it is not from within me, something has happened

MATA HARI

37, exotic dancer and courtesan

JACK JOHNSON

35, world heavyweight boxing champion

in a room at the Hotel Friedrichshof, Berlin, during Johnson's exile from the United States, 1913

MATA HARI

I dance: I dance for Shiva I dance to ask Shiva to destroy me once more I am Mata Hari born of a temple dancer who died at my birth and I was but thirteen when I myself first danced naked for Shiva at the temple but Shiva destroys me and remakes me yet again and I am Princess Anuba sending her lover to the bottom of the sea and he returns savaged by sea monsters and dying but he has in his bloody hand my heart's desire, the sacred black pearl, and the black pearl has become a man and has entered now into Anuba and I take him and he is part of me and Shiva destroys me as I dance once more, I am the temple smoke and I am the sea and I am the falling veils and I am my naked body, and what I am not is Margaretha Geertruida Zelle, and I am not a Dutch wife to a man who beats me, and I am not the mother of a son poisoned to death in Java by the husband of my husband's lover, I am not, I am dead, I am destroyed and I live again

JACK

the tenor is in my head and he is singing sweet, this troubadour, this wanderer with no place in the world, and he knows how things be and he sings *Deserto sulla terra, col rio destino in guerra* – I heard him a dozen times in Paris – and I got the words up now in English and I can see myself back a few years in Reno and James J. Jeffries and me is waiting to start and the crowd is chanting *Kill the nigger* and the band is playing *All Coons Look Alike to Me* and then suddenly I step forward before the bell, I go out in the center of the ring and I start to sing in a voice so loud they all shut the hell up and they listen and I sing *All alone on the earth, I'll go forty-five rounds with my evil fate* and they don't make another sound till I'm done and I only need fifteen of those rounds and I'm still the champ, and so is Mister Verdi, me and him are the heavyweight champs of the world

GEORGE HERMAN "BABE" RUTH
21, baseball player

JOSEPHINE RUGGLES
24, prostitute

in the Chambre Rouge at Lulu White's all-octoroon Mahogany Hall, Storyville, New Orleans, 1916

BABE

a bat in my hands a hickory bat long and heavy and the color of tobacco spit and I'm about to hit my first one and it's little Jack Warhop on the mound throwing his rise ball and it's the third inning in the Polo Grounds, and say but I'm swell at last, it's fine for me as a pitcher breaking off curves on the corner of the plate, but try to slip one by me with my bat in my hand and see what I can do, and here I am now in a fancy bed with a girl and she might as well see it all, she might as well see what I can do, and the same for all you girls in all the fancy rooms and in all the cheap cribs in Storyville, I'm out of the goddamn boy's home at last, out of St. Mary's, through being an orphan with two parents working a tavern across town, and now Mom's dead for real, and little Jack is standing sixty feet away and this is how you get it all back: your feet close together and your right shoulder swung around to him and the bat sitting easy on your left shoulder nuzzled in the crook of your neck and he winds and throws, and his rise ball is what he's got that says I don't belong where I am, and I can see the ball spinning, I can count the stitches, and what I do starts in my stomach, it starts in the center of me right there and it flows easy into my arms and hips and legs and I hitch back and glide on through and the groove is there and it's sweeter than any pussy, me passing into this invisible place, and there's a little push against the bat and a swell chunking sound and the ball is rushing off and up and up and it flies fast and far and farther still and it falls into the straw hats deep in the right-field stands and it's my first home run and I am still feeling its kiss, it kissed me hard and wet right on my bat

JOSEPHINE

he yawps and grunts, this overgrown boy, and of a sudden he cries *Say but I'm swell* and now is off to whooping again, but you're not that swell I can tell you and I just try to hear beyond him, the piano trickling up from the parlor downstairs, Lulu has let a colored boy in tonight to play and he's doing it fine and they're down there dancing the ragtime one-step on the parquet floor, not the mudbuggers like this boy but the Americans from Uptown in evening clothes, and I could be doing it with them, doing what I really do: pulling the arm of a true swell around my waist and facing him a little off center and taking his left hand in my right and finding that easy-glide spot – our hands just a bit away from us and a little up from the waist, my right elbow slightly bent, my left hand cupping behind his right shoulder, my back straight upright, my heels together and my toes turned

outward, perfect, like finding the lay of me in bed when I'm finally alone and can sleep – and tonight we'll do the Castle Walk so I go up onto the balls of my feet and stiffen my legs and I pull ever so slightly with my palm behind his shoulder and with the tips of my fingers at the back of his hand and he doesn't even know I'm leading and we're off, stepping away long and smooth and quick around and around Lulu White's whorehouse parlor and nobody does the one-step like Jo and it's all for free

ERNEST HEMINGWAY
23, writer

CÉLINE GAUTHIER
34, prostitute

in a brothel on the rue de la Huchette upon Hemingway's return to Paris to confirm that his wife, Hadley, had indeed lost virtually all of his manuscripts, including carbon copies, on a train, DECEMBER 4, 1922

ERNEST

how did it begin, the one I ache for the most:

We waited in the woods in the shadows of the trees the color of

They told us to stop the Germans from crossing the bridge and we waited in the woods. The shadows were

The shadows of the trees were gray. There were barrage balloons in the sky

We waited for the Germans while the barrage balloons floated over the Austrian lines

We waited in the woods and the shadows were the color of

We waited in the woods. The color of the shadows was gray

We waited in the woods for the Germans

The shadows

We waited in the woods for the Germans. The shadows of the trees were the color of gun metal. The barrage balloons

We waited in the woods for the Germans to try to cross the stone bridge. The shadows of the trees were the color of gun metal. Against the distant mountains we could see the barrage balloons floating over the Austrian lines. I felt I was already dead because she put every word I'd ever written into a valise and then lost it on a fucking train

CÉLINE

I wait and later I will go to the café and I will sit in the corner table, I will drink a calvados slowly, keeping my palms on the tabletop, my hands will rest on the coolness of the slate tabletop and I will watch Bernard behind the zinc bar, he will wipe the top of the bar lightly in long elegant strokes, in the long mirror behind the bar I will look at the bald spot on the back of his head, I know how the spot has grown since I first came to this restaurant and the zinc bar has grown darker, from a dark gray to nearly black, and I will not see myself in the mirror from the table where I sit, everything else is in the mirror but I am not, the calvados will taste of apples and a little bit of pear and I will drink it slowly and there will be nothing in my mind, the nothing of the tabletop and the nothing of the zinc bar and the nothing of the bare spot on Bernard's head and the nothing of the trees silhouetted outside against the electric light and the nothing of sitting very still and drinking slowly

JOSEPHINE BAKER
19, dancer

GEORGES SIMENON
22, writer

in her rooms at the Hôtel Fournet, Montmartre, Paris, JANUARY 1926

GEORGES

oo la la la la la la la the butt, the most famous butt in Paris, sweetly compliant now, silent, but redolent of its fame onstage: this butt can laugh, this butt can sing, this butt can carry on a sublime dialog within its twinned self in its own language, one cheek quivering and then the other: *I am so beautiful my sister* yes yes I am too my sister *this city is watching us entranced and we are both so beautiful* we are and we are so chic wearing flamingo feathers or bananas as if they were a Paul Poiret or a Jean Patou we are so very chic *but we are even more beautiful utterly naked for we are the perfection of curves* ah yes we are the globes to the angles in art deco *it's true sister we are modern but we are also savage we are also primitive we are the jungle we are the night we are the call of birds* – wait, wait, what has Josephine done to her Georges – I am a man of words, nineteen novels already, full of elegant and simple words, and yet in praise I have just had her butt make bird calls: I have gone mad

JOSEPHINE

oo la la how they want me to be blacker and blacker, even Georges, his pipe on the bed stand and his hands all over my naked butt and I just have to make my cheeks tremble there and he will cry out in French as wildly as Genevieve and she will answer from across the room in Monkey, but I keep them both quiet tonight, I am myself quiet inside and I cannot stop my mind, for tonight I danced as I always dance – some Charleston some Black Bottom, some Mess Around and Tack Annie and Shim Sham Break and some things I tell myself are Africa but are St. Louis, for all that, are me just knocking my knees and camel-walking and vibrating my butt and flailing my arms and legs – I danced as always but at the same time I was somewhere up in the balcony with these ravenous French watching me dance, which is something I almost never do, but just because I dance in a trance most of the time don't mean the dance has anything to do with what I am and what I am driven to want, which is something I got from St. Louis, as well: my hair is conked flat and lacquered, which the French don't understand the meaning of, and at the end I cross my eyes at them and I flap my arms like a backyard chicken, and they don't understand that either, but after it's all over and the night is gone and the sun comes up in Paris, each morning I get into my hotel bathtub and I soak in hot water and goat's milk and lemon and honey and Eau de Javel that they scour their sinks with and I soak and I soak till my pussy's on fire just so I can be white

81

JEAN-PAUL SARTRE

24, recent graduate in philosophy from the École Normale Supérieure

SIMONE DE BEAUVOIR

21, recent graduate in philosophy from the Sorbonne

in her fifth-floor rented room at 91 avenue Denfert-Rochereau, Montparnasse, Paris, 1929

JEAN-PAUL

too much of her too much silk skin, brick nipple, face of porcelain, too much of this room too much cane chair and claw-foot table and orange divan too much orange-papered wall and foxed window shade, too much café still clinging like the smell of pipe smoke to us in too much wood-plank bed too much stack of café saucer, too much mirror showing mirror showing mirror too much gilt frame, too much sheep-back hunching of bodies all around, too much night street after the café too much plane tree and shadow of plane tree on the cobbled street too much hooded lamp and boulder row of Renault, too much stairway and crystal of bare lightbulbs and shadow down the hall and hard brass doorknobs, all of it too much, all of it with no reason for being there, too much gape of her lips, too much gape of her loins, too much of her and too little of me: I think I'm going to be sick

SIMONE

one eye dead, one eye drifts away, neither of them looking at me, and I thrash in the vague light on the crumpled sheet not from his touch but from his sightlessness: I have vanished and my invisibility shudders through me like sex and I can hear him thinking inside that wall-eyed head sitting on that tiny body with its tiny parts and he knows me not, but he knows he knows me not, and I know he knows he knows me not, and so I am even more alone in this bed in this room in this shuddering trembling body of mine and I am free

MILTON BERLE
23, comedian

AIMEE SEMPLE MCPHERSON
40, evangelist

in her apartment in Santa Monica, after a Los Angeles charity benefit, 1930

MILTON

this is a novelty act on the Orpheum Circuit if there ever was one, the sexy Christian pastor and the good Jewish boy – well not such a good boy, though Mama looks the other way and just packs our bags when I'm hosing down a girl – *I think sex is better than logic, but I can't prove it* – this is more like a freak act, not big enough to close before intermission, this, but maybe we'd go on after the three-spot, presenting the Wandering Youth with the Giant Dong and Sister Aimee with the dust of the Arizona Desert from her phantom kidnapping clinging to her ankles – and pretty ankles they are – *The sex was so good that even the neighbors had a cigarette* – but it's a freak act all right, with the candles burning over there on the dresser and the silver cross and the framed crucifixion – don't look at me, Sister, I didn't do it – *A conscience is what hurts when all your other parts are feeling good* – all that chestnut hair of yours, smelling like the sea – I'd be happy to give your way a try, but *It's hard to be religious when certain people have never been incinerated by a lightning bolt – and you know who you are, you're not laughing right now – what are you, an audience or an oil painting?* – maybe it's just that you know the real me, Sister, you and the silent audience both – forget my baby face, I've been doing this a long time, a long long time already, shtupping and shticking and I'm starting to feel old – *At least I don't drink, I learned that from my Jewish mother, who never touches the stuff, alcohol interferes with her suffering – Jesus may love me, but everybody else thinks I'm a jerk – Sure, there was a time when everybody believed in God, and the Church ruled the world, it was called the Dark Ages – I believe you, Sister, Jesus is coming, but I'm coming first*

AIMEE

my back bends upward and I can imagine my body turning all the colors, from my toes to the crown of my head, from red to orange to yellow and green and then to blue and indigo and to violet: I am a rainbow, I am a covenant, my Lord *Amen* a covenant *Amen* You put me in this body and the flesh yearns for You and You are the word made flesh and You are also the flesh made word *He shall lie all night betwixt my breasts* and You are present in all your creation, Lord, You are in the sparrow and You are in the beggar by the road and You are in the comedian from the vaudeville stage and with Your infinite tenderness You understood the woman at the well and You understood Your dear Mary Magdalene *Let him kiss me with the kisses of his mouth, for thy love is better than wine* and You understand

me, who aches and thrills for You and who cries out Your love, Lord, to the world, for Your gospel is not the gospel of fear and hell and damnation but the gospel of reconciliation and of love, You move in me You fill me up, my Lord, I am full of love for even the least of Your creatures, and this one happens to have a part like the tower of Lebanon which looketh toward Damascus and I hold him close so he can hear the heart in my breast which beats now madly in love of You and he will listen *Amen* and I will soar to You *Amen* and he will believe *Amen* and I say *Amen* and *Amen* and *Amen*

CLYDE BARROW

25, outlaw

BONNIE PARKER

23, outlaw

*in a cabin in the woods near Shreveport, Louisiana, on the eve of their
death by police ambush, 1934*

CLYDE

some gump I knew wanted to be a tough guy and had no chance, but I was interested in his sister who they said had slipped on the ice and broke her arm and she had it in a sling, and so I go over to the gump's house thinking to make time with the girl now that she's one arm short, and there's noise in the kitchen and I get touchy real fast because they also say the laws is looking for me cause of the little getting-started jobs I've been pulling in McLennan County, and she says *Go on in and meet my friend* and there she is with her back to me, and she turns and the window is behind her and it lights up her strawberry hair like it's a fiery crown and it sure starts to burning in me right away, and the first thing I do after saying my name and she says hers is to reach into my coat pocket and pull out my pistol and lay it on the table that's between us, a 1911-model Colt .45, and this is just to make it clear to her from the first who I am and what she's getting into with me cause it don't take me more than about three seconds with this tiny girl with the red ringlets and the freckles and that smart-aleck half-smile to know she's the one, though I never dream how far she's going to go with me, but the first thing out of my mouth after we get our names and my Colt on the table is *Here is my honest declaration to you, Miss Parker, I am a dangerous man to anybody who gets in the way of me taking what I want and pissing on the shoes of the government that has took everything the working stiffs have got, which also means that nobody messes with any woman who is with me* and she moves that half-smile from one side of her mouth to the other, and little did I know that one day I'd give her a .32-caliber Harrington and Richardson top-break pistol for her purse and her eyes would fill with grateful tears

BONNIE

I hear a noise behind me while I'm standing in Daisy Wickham's kitchen trying to open a jar of Ovaltine at the sink, and my head is full of the darnedest thick mud from the sun coming off the dirty snow outside and from the ticking of a clock and the dripping from the faucet, and I'm sinking fast in that mud cause of this being what my life is – making Ovaltine and hearing these sounds that ask me to just go ahead and beat my head on that window till it cracks – but this noise behind me is footsteps and somehow I know it ain't Daisy, and I turn and there he is with his brown hair slicked back, though a curl of it has figured out how to drop down on his forehead, and his eyes are dark but they might as well be bright red with fire cause they

are burning their way into my brain, and he says *I'm Clyde Barrow* and I say *I'm Bonnie Parker* and he pulls a pistol out of his coat and lays it on the table and I don't even for a second worry about a thing cause he's giving off something into the air so sweet as to make me want to wiggle my hips, but I keep real still and he says *I mean to be honest with you, Miss Parker, I am a dangerous man but I am a strong man and I can get things for you so that you and me won't ever turn into working stiffs and I can take care of you forever* and I don't know how long forever will be with Clyde Barrow but I am ready to say yes right then

ADOLF HITLER
46, Reichskanzler and Führer

INGA ARVAD
22, journalist

in his office at the Reich Chancellery, during an interview for a Danish newspaper, Berlin, 1935

ADOLF

pigeons outside the window murmuring at the seed laid out, crumbs in the corners for the mice, Wolf sleeping in the outer office on a leather chair, dreaming – how I wish I could dream his dog's dreams, hanging out of the car with the wind lifting his ears, running fast without even moving his legs – this little mouse beneath me, a perfect Aryan mouse, I will not eat you up, little mouse, I will eat cabbage and lentils and peas instead, not my little mouse, and at my temples I begin to burn and now all my face is burning and I cannot breathe and I cannot sleep and when I do, hands are upon me and my father's whip, my mother's hands and her wild eyes and my face is aflame from what the social democrats have done to us and what the liberals have done and the reactionary monarchists and the capitalists and the communists and the Jews, the Jews, what the Jews have done to us what the Jews have done to all of us and eighty million voices cry out as one and it is for me and they lift their arms and they are inside me, the German people, and they are like a woman, needy, needing, needing, needy beyond thought, needy for strong hands upon them, needy for Fatherland for Father for Empire for the great German Empire needy for Hitler and Hitler will feed the mice and he will kill the beasts

INGA

how can this be, for soon I stopped taking notes and then I stopped asking questions and I am on the pale plush rug in the middle of his office floor: it was his voice, the unlikely quietness of it, the pain of it, he crossed his hands on his chest and lifted his eyes upward to the ceiling and far beyond, and he was hurt, this man for whom vast throngs of Germans cry out to command them, but for me his eyes lifted in pain and then returned unwavering to me, confiding deeply in me, those eyes came upon me and did not waver and at first they seemed pale blue, a fragile bird's-egg blue, but now they were bright and dark, nearly violet, and these eyes would not move from me and I capped my pen and I trembled at his need and then his voice rose and he began to fill the room with a guttural litany of rage and his crossed arms unfurled and his hands flared and then clenched into fists and leaped up to frame his face and his power filled the room, and even as I trembled in fear I knew that his showing me this was an intimacy, as well: he commanded me fiercely and he needed me desperately, needs me even now, for this brief time, he is strong enough to hold me safe and weak enough for me to hold him safe, and so

INGA ARVAD

29, journalist

JOHN F. KENNEDY

24, ensign, U.S. Navy Intelligence

in room 132, Fort Sumter Hotel, Charleston, South Carolina,
FEBRUARY 1942

INGA

how can this be, this long skinny boy on his back and it's simple inside that brain of his *Inga Binga hop on let's go* and that was on his mind even as he told me that the FBI is following me and he said he knows I'm not a Nazi spy but Hoover hates the Kennedys and will destroy the number-two son through me but that's okay by him, his big brother Joe can go ahead and be President without him, he's ready to teach history somewhere with his Inga, his Lutheran-former-Miss-Denmark-older-woman-divorcée wife, and to hell with Mama Rose and Papa Joe and he can play touch football with his students, so he said *Inga Binga hop on* and now I let my hair fall into his face and he's always contented for this to be quick, but I won't let him move yet, not this time: his eyes are gray as a winter sky and I'm bundled up in the Tivoli Gardens and there's only the snow and that sky and I'm feeling warm about some toothsome schoolboy and I'm thinking about when the first time will happen and how it will be simple when it does and how there is nothing I need to think about beyond that

JOHN

young Jack Junior doesn't like to wait standing at attention and if it weren't Inga Binga slowing us down he'd just have to do his business and be done with it, but it's okay since it's her and I'm not sure why, because the world's full of pussies and going after them is like wanting a landslide, getting all the votes, shaking a hand and winning the voter at the other end of it and then the next and the next until every last one of them loves you, but my Inga and her pussy are the whole damn electorate in one, it clasps JJ in its grasp and whispers that it alone is all that counts, and standing now at attention I think perhaps I can be content, I think I can leave the ceaseless striving to the rest of my family, I can give up everything just to be happy like that, but I know how it works, JJ, I'm sorry but I know how it works, when she lets me move – and she soon will – and as soon as you've got what you want, then I'll want to be President again

J. EDGAR HOOVER

53, Director of the Federal Bureau of Investigation

CLYDE TOLSON

48, Associate Director

in Tolson's apartment at the Wardman Park Hotel, Washington, DC, NOVEMBER 1946

J. EDGAR

a congressman now, my young Jack, and he will go far and he's all mine, I should have played my favorite of the recordings this afternoon, but it's all right, tomorrow perhaps, and even now I can hear it clearly: the mousy squeaking of the bedsprings as he lies down – on his back, where he will remain, from spinal troubles – and the rustle of his terry-cloth towel being thrown off, he's been walking around the bedroom in a towel after his shower and he never puts his clothes back on with her and he can't wait any longer and he lies down and throws off the towel *Inga Binga hop on let's go* he says and I rewind and I listen to the brief silence after the words, I rewind and it is silent for a few moments, I rewind and he says *Inga Binga hop on let's go* and then I can hear the brief silence of his solitary nakedness, and this time it's not Inga Arvad who approaches his bed but a different woman and he is surprised, but he gives her a close look as she stands before him and he smiles at this new woman, who is older, yes, but she pleasantly evokes a mother figure who nevertheless radiates sensuality, which he desperately needs, and her face is perhaps a bit mannish, but that's appealing too, he likes its sense of command, and he admires her sexy but conservative fluffy black dress with flounces and her feather boa and he says *Hop on* and I do and he is all mine

CLYDE

in a glass cabinet across the room, our two machine guns – his hanging above mine – from New Orleans and our busting in on Creepy Karpis and his gang, and on the table beside the bed, my weekly orchid – this time he chose a *Cypripedium*, with green and brown speckles on its throat – and he would have led the charge through Creepy's door but for me, but for taking care of his Clyde, holding us back behind the other agents, and when we went in, guns ready, it was shoulder to shoulder, the Director and me, and that night he had Dubonnet carnations delivered to our hotel room and we put them in our button holes and we went out and we ate oysters in the Vieux Carré and the press were popping their bulbs at us, the hero G-men, and little did they know the truth about this great and powerful man, how he was a machine-gun man and he was a flower man and he needed me to hold him

ALBERT EINSTEIN

66, physicist

MARGARITA KONENKOVA

51, Soviet spy and wife of Russian expatriate sculptor and fellow spy Sergei Konenkov

in Albert's house at 112 Mercer Street, Princeton, New Jersey, JULY 17, 1945

ALBERT

I lost the office pool Teller lost the pool and I didn't know if his voice was fuzzy from telephonic static or from grief, and then my dear Margarita arrives moments later and I hope I can do what I have to do – I want to do for her what I have to do – but Teller lost the pool, and so it has happened, the night before the first one went off he said they would put a silver dollar each on the limit of the chain reaction and he said he'd make the uncollectible bet – that there would be no limit, that it would not stop till the earth was incinerated – and if he was right, I would know, and if he was wrong, he would tell me he was wrong so I could know what I am supposed not to know, that it's happened, and we did what we had to do, we have it and Hitler doesn't, but Hitler's done for anyway now and we have it and I am afraid we will find a way to make it useful and I wish I had been a cobbler, I wish what I had to do was be a cobbler; I wish we'd all been cobblers and we had filled the world with shoes

MARGARITA

he laughs so abruptly sometimes, so ringingly, it's as if all his thoughts have gathered together so hotly and so brilliantly that they explode but it's all right because in the end he finds the universe hilarious, and he walks so distractedly sometimes, dragging the tip of his umbrella along the iron fences of Mercer Street, but if he misses a single picket he stops and returns to touch it, almost tenderly, this Professor Einstein, this Albert, and it all befuddles me, it diverts me from my mission, but I want to get this straight: if the light from a star was our train compartment right now and Albert and I were doing this while moving at the speed of light and if Joe Stalin was watching from far behind us, would we actually be having sex like a truly connected man and woman and it was only old Joe who mistakenly sees Albert in achingly slow motion, not getting it up no matter how hard I try, and sees my eyes slowly filling with tears for not being able to get him really to love me

RICHARD MILHOUS NIXON
40, Vice President of the United States

THELMA CATHERINE "PAT" NIXON
41, his wife

in the bedroom of their home in Washington, DC, 1953

RICHARD

Mother was a saint a Quaker saint *I'm ready to go, Mother,* I'm sixteen and as always I rose at four in the terrible dark and I went to Los Angeles and I bought the lettuce and the squash and the snap beans for the grocery and I have returned, with the sun, and I'm ready now to go to school, starched-collared and Windsor-knotted, and I say *Mother I'm ready* and she comes to me and she rises on her toes and she brings her face very near mine and she sniffs, she checks to make sure I am free of halitosis, and she says *Only a faint sweetness* and my breath catches at this, as it always does, I am clean and I will cause no offense and I will succeed on this day and in the night I am caught: I am clutching at myself beneath the sheet and she is standing in the doorway, just come in from closing the store and she's still wearing her coat, a plain cloth coat, a plain Quaker cloth coat, and at her feet our dog pants and slobbers, our cocker spaniel dog, and I am caught and it makes it all the sweeter, I lift my hands from beneath the sheets to show her, I hold them above my head and I say *I am not a masturbator* but I am throbbing on even as I say this and she turns and she goes and she knows and it is sweet and tonight Pat stood in the door in her Republican cloth coat and she brought Checkers, as I had asked, and I was caught and it was very sweet

PAT

who am I beneath this coat, he did not ask for me to be naked beneath it but I am, I am always naked, beneath a coat, a dress, beneath my smile and the popping of flashbulbs and the clamor of voices, and he is done, my Dick, my Dick is done already in his solitude, the coat is still closed though I am naked beneath it and against my face his breath is faint and abrasive with Listerine and he is silent and I slide my arm beneath him and he does not move and we are young and nothing has begun, we are a young lawyer and a young typing teacher, a couple of amateur actors at the Whittier Community Theatre, and he takes me aside, into the dark of the wings into the smell of mildew and fresh paint and canvas and he says *This is how you make yourself cry* and he teaches me what his college drama coach taught him, to concentrate hard on getting a lump in your throat, and after the lesson he furrows his brow and he clenches his face and makes his lump and he begins to cry, great large tears roll down Dick Nixon's face and beneath them I know he is sad beyond expressing and I wipe at the tears though I know they are fake

JOSEPH R. MCCARTHY
44, U.S. Senator

JEAN KERR MCCARTHY
29, his wife and long-time research assistant

on their honeymoon at Spanish Key in the British West Indies,
SEPTEMBER 1953

JEAN

oh Mama shut up, oh Mama all permed and buttoned tight, oh Mama on your divan covered in vinyl to keep the flower upholstery pristine and unsoiled and untouched, oh Mama your voice fills the gathering dimness of your living room, the low-watt bulbs turned off until the light of day has vanished utterly, oh Mama shut up, stop your last-minute warnings, thinking I'm still a virgin, stop your talk of sex and the male conspiracy of it, its infiltration, its invasion, he is heavy on me yes, he is heavy as you said, yes, but shut up Mama, he is sweating yes and I want to rub it off my face and shoulders with the back of my wrist, hard, yes, but shut up, Mama, I am married to him and he is a great man and he will save our country but I cannot even look at him in this moment while I'm hearing your voice, Mama, so I turn my face away from him for now and I say to you *Mama, please shut the hell up*

JOE

her eyes just moved, she should be looking at me and only at me but her eyes shifted to the left, off the bed, and she has put facts in my head and words in my mouth plenty these past few years of the crusade and she has felt my wrath and tasted my kisses and so she should know better than to take her eyes off me in the middle of me plucking her chicken, churning her butter, plowing her field with a blunt blade, so there is a reason to watch when her eyes shift off the bed at a time like this and I should stop and see what's up but things just keep going on even though it could be that she heard a faint scuff of footsteps outside the door or a rasp of a pass key in the lock, someone ready to bust in blazing away with their Kalashnikov AK-47 automatic weapons, whose development and manufacture were financed secretly by the March of Dimes, thanks to Franklin Roosevelt, whose own eyes shifted away from the cameras at Yalta to give Joe Stalin a wink, and she's still looking away and maybe the enemy is already in the room, maybe the enemy is right beneath us, under the bed, waiting, maybe my wife herself is one of them, maybe there's a man under our bed and she's just waiting for me to be done and waiting for me to fall asleep and then she will tap twice lightly on the mattress and he will come up and he will slide in beside her and he will whisper to her in a language I do not understand

ROBERT F. KENNEDY

36, Attorney General of the United States

MARILYN MONROE

35, actress

in the Santa Monica beach house of Kennedy's brother-in-law, Peter Lawford, 1962

ROBERT

my high hectoring whine let you be cool and calm and I elected you, and I keep your secrets secret – your back and your painkillers and your women – and they love you, the women, even when they're being hustled away five minutes later with that dazed flutter in their eyes from it being over so quick, and in a foggy February morning off the coast of Maine I leap into the waves and you dare not follow and the cold nearly stops my heart but I do not care: I am gaunt and I brood and my eyes goggle slightly more than yours – the difference between handsome and creepy – and I was Runt to the old man and I was Little Bobby the Devout to Mother and I am Black Robert to you and – mea culpa, mea maxima culpa – I am with this woman, and it's true I am with her only after you, only because of you, but to her I am The General and I am at ten minutes and counting and I dare not ask but I can hear her saying inside her head *Oh, General, yes yes you are ever so much better in bed than the President*

MARILYN

nothing but the slowing of my heart, nothing but filling up in the hungry place, and the hunger stops at once as if it was nothing to start with, but the fullness inside that part of me makes another kind of nothing and I float with that, I can turn my head as I float and I can feel my face moving, my eyes falling on something – a clock on a blond wood chest of drawers – and I feel my face turn again and the ceiling is spackled and the nothing that is usually trying to claw its way out of my chest, out of my wrists, out of my throat and eyes and brain, the nothing that I am, the nothing worth anything: that nothing is gone and the nothing that remains is some man, a man of a certain bulk, of a certain scent, of a certain murmuring, a certain sighing, a certain panting and wanting and wanting – wanting me – and to me it is nothing, but the nothing it pours into me lets me close my eyes and rest a few moments from what I am

WILLIAM JEFFERSON CLINTON

24, law student

HILLARY DIANE RODHAM

23, law student

*in his second-floor bedroom at a rented beach house in Milford,
Connecticut, late spring, 1971*

HILLARY

this had to be done eventually and the personal is political all right and if your underwear and your armpits and your hairdo and your shoes are political then choosing to fuck a specific man in a specific bed on a specific day is political and it's merely political and he's the one all right because everything we talk about makes it clear: McGovern next year and somebody after that and somebody after that and somebody after that and then he and I may choose to fuck in Lincoln's bed or on the eagle on the floor in the Oval Office, and I don't care if that's the next time we do this, to be honest with myself, but I choose this time and I will choose some others in between because one day we'll be fucking on the eagle and there's a soft knock at the door and the secretary knows not to barge in and she says *Madame President, the Soviet premier is on the phone*

BILL

this has to be done at this point, though I miss the surprise, I miss the gasp from a grab of their tits or the dropping of my pants when they least expect it, but there are plenty of others for that, this one's not in her body yet, which is cute enough in spite of her severe qualms, but at least I did get her to shave her legs pretty quick and I can sometimes surprise her into a brief silence with some line of reasoning – McGovern's chances for the nomination or Ping-Pong as metaphor for Chinese-American relations or some other thing that comes to my lips as quick as kisses – and I did at least rip those red-frame glasses off her face, and Coltrane is playing in my head – *A Love Supreme* – and my lips go itchy and not for Hillary's mouth on mine but for an abandoned ambition, me on the sax forever, though the twinge passes quickly now because Coltrane's power is detached from his own moment-to-moment life, even in the clubs, the ones he's got hold of are out beyond the glare of lights, beyond his direct touch, I was right to let that go, let go of being a surgeon, too, where you exercise your ultimate power only when they don't even know it from the anesthetics, I know the path for me and this girl knows it too, better than anybody else – I can see crowds, great large crowds to wade into and to touch – she's smart and she's tough and I know she won't put up with certain things from me and I don't want to lose her but before she's done here I've got to figure out how to get on top

ELVIS PRESLEY
42, singer

HOLLY SINGLETON
20, admirer

in his dressing room at the Market Square Arena, Indianapolis, Indiana, after what would be his last public performance, JUNE 26, 1977

HOLLY

he was singing all in white in this kind of jumpsuit with a big golden something on him, like the sun, but it was split in half by his bare chest and it was about driving me crazy to see that, and now listen to me, I'm naked with him and I should be memorizing his body but instead I'm trying to remember him from the stage even though he's right here with me in his own private dressing room and he's touching me and I can look at what I've always dreamed about seeing but I can't stop *thinking* about seeing him instead of actually opening my darn eyes and *seeing*, like what if you had ten minutes with Jesus and you kept thinking *Wow here I am with Jesus, Wow God's Chosen Son is sitting right in front of me* instead of going *Jesus, is it okay to use my tongue when I kiss my boyfriend* and *Please Jesus, my mama's about driving me crazy with her criticism, is it dishonoring her to tell her to stop even if I don't actually say "shut up"* and look what I'm doing now, I'm thinking about talking to Jesus when *Elvis* is right here, and my head is so full of stupid thoughts that I'm not even seeing him, and even thinking about how my thoughts are stupid is stupid because it's still more of not seeing him, but really, if I do see him, if I do actually look at Elvis Presley's naked body, how will I ever go on with the rest of my life

ELVIS

you're how it used to be, pretty lady, me singing like it's just for some new girl in the front row, but all this goes way back, Mama and me sitting in chairs in the little patch of grass at the Lauderdale Courts and she's been waiting up for me and she's past being mad, she knows I been on Beale Street, at dusk I went on and walked out of Pinchgut and down Lauderdale to Beale, and like I do, I'm moving from door to door at the clubs, listening, and somewhere along the way somebody who knew to see me finally says *Let that white boy in* and I go in trembling and it's Arthur Crudup singing and he is singing to me and he is singing about me, this colored man with his dark angel voice who knows every pain in the world, and I come back and before Mama can say anything I sit down alongside her, and behind us and above us there's voices shouting at each other and there's a dog barking somewhere and there's a woman's crying, too, coming from a window and a boat whistle from the river and I lean to Mama and I touch her arm, and this is just for her, and though I'm feeling already that someday I'll do this for everybody and I'll do it with a beat and I'll move my body to the life of it, for now I sing just to her, real soft and slow *That's all right now, Mama, anyway you do*

DIANA
25, Princess of Wales

CHARLES PHILIP ARTHUR GEORGE
37, Prince of Wales and Earl of Chester, Duke of Cornwall, Duke of Rothesay, Earl of Carrick and Baron of Renfrew, Lord of the Isles, Prince and Great Steward of Scotland, heir apparent to the British throne

at King Juan Carlos's Marivent Palace near Palma, Majorca, AUGUST 1986, *for the last time*

DIANA

now that he's begun this and is humphing softly in confusion, trying to work out just why he's even trying, I need to breathe deep and curl my toes on the edge of the pool at Park House and there's a smell of the salt sea in the air and there are yew trees and silver birch and pine all around and I saw a young fox in the morning and he and I stood on the lawn and looked at each other for a long long while and I stand now waiting for just the right moment to dive, my arms outstretched, bending over the water at the deep end, and all my dolls have been properly walked in their pram and all the animals on my bed have been stroked and put just so and Daddy is puttering in the garden and my sisters are lounging in the sunlight and my brother is napping inside and Mummy hasn't legged it yet – I don't even know it's coming – so I wait at the edge of the pool for just the right moment and I don't understand that it would be ever so advisable just to plunge on in and glide to the bottom and not come back up at all, not at all, for it will never be anywhere near as nice as this again, ever

CHARLES

Uncle Dickie, how can I disagree with you, and Mum, you are the paragon of Uncle Dickie's advice are you not, how unsettled one should be if another man has touched your wife before you have found her, how disturbing for her sweet-charactered allure, for her fresh-budded tenderness to have been known fully by another man who shall then carry around forever the intimate memory of the King's wife in his mind to take out and fondle and treasure as if it were all still his, and so she is thus, my wife, but she is gaunt from her virginity, she is chlorine and ammonia and antiseptic, and of course she weeps and faints and has no sense of me because there is no sense in her of any other life, no sense of any other man by which to measure me, to give meaning to any loving word she would say to me: she is slick and untouched as a fish and I would cling to a horse who's been ridden

ROOSTER

2, stud

CHICKEN

1, roaster

in a barnyard in Alabama, 2000

ROOSTER

they used to look at me different, the sweet chicks – I know that much – not so detached, not so stupid, but they didn't used to have wings and feathers, either – I peck at little bits of that previous life I must have lived like pecking at yummy pieces of overlooked corn out in the midst of the grit and pebbles oh boy, and now I'm on her and oh boy oh boy, and yes the chicks used to be – how did I stand it? – utterly featherless, utterly, and they used to look at me with pleading awe and wonder, which was a better look – why the difference now? – I was rich then, oh yes, and I had splendid plumage, I'm sure, great red hackles and a tall comb, I was a magnificent looking something or other, a cock, a cocksman – oh ruffle and strut oh ruffle and strut and hop on and I am really something right now and I'm fucking and clucking and she's loving it like crazy because I am the man around here, and over there beyond the fence are the featherless ones, who, in spite of their puny plumage – or perhaps because of it – seem very familiar to me, and suddenly I understand: they are watching me and they are listening to me cluck and they are laughing at the sounds I make that they don't understand, but I know that someday they will be sweet little chicks, too, and I'll be waiting for them

CHICKEN

eggy eggy eggy and then the little fluffs will come out and I will hover and fluff up too and they will huddle beneath me and this is a very useful cock I think, he flares his tail and puffs up his hackles very nice and he struts very nice and sometimes I wonder what that's all about why I am impressed with that and then I wonder what is this farm thing going on and then it's like, whoa, was that a stop sign I blew through, and there's a big commotion all around me and I think I better call my agent, and then I go, like, what's a stop sign? what's an agent? and just as I am about to answer myself, the thoughts are gone – these moments of confusion don't come so often anymore – I just wish this dude would get it over with because I've got a lot of pecking in the dirt to do, like it's all I can do to score some corn around here

KEVIN SMITH

32, advertising copywriter

JULIA HANSON SMITH

30, graphic designer

in their apartment in Brooklyn, the night of SEPTEMBER 11, 2001

KEVIN

I know the night is filled with smoke and with fire and I would not have thought it would be my wife clinging to me now because of what I have done: I should have gone out the door last night after my clumsiness, she was half-turned at the stove, the steam rising before her from the boiling rice, and all that I'd planned carefully to say came out impulsively, simply, badly, *I am in love* and she knew it was not her and she laid the lid on the pot and she turned her back to me and later we sat in chairs in the dark of our living room for a long while, the pot charred black on the stove, and I did not go and then it was this morning and then the long day and I am in love and I think it is not with her, but tonight, in this moment, we dare not change a thing

JULIA

how can it be so quiet from across the river, if you do not make yourself look you might never realize the terrible thing going on, and he and I do not look, we know but we choose for this night not to look, even into our own hearts, though I can hear faintly through the wall someone weeping and from another place the murmur of television voices, and I see myself standing in an open window high above the city: I cannot go back inside and I cannot step into the empty air, and from this distance I am only a figure standing in a window, I can only try to imagine what I am feeling

GEORGE W. BUSH

57, President of the United States

LAURA BUSH

57, First Lady

in the master bedroom of the White House, MARCH 2004

LAURA

the Nancy Reagan wallpaper here is very nice, actually – all the peacocks and roosters and bluebirds hand-painted on Chinese paper – she was a good strong Republican woman – is that my cell phone? – no, just a ringing in my ears – I'll have to hold my nostrils and blow when I get a chance, which won't be long – wallpaper, wallpaper – I'm not sure about the wallpaper design in the Lincoln Bedroom, but that pallid lemon stuff will go and also the carpet, with those flowers so pale they look dead – a diamond-grid English Wilton's the thing for the floor, bold Victorian greens and purples and yellows like the sunlight – and a new mattress for the bed, though I better not let Mother Bush know or she'll have one of her conniptions, since it was she who finally replaced the horsehair, but her mattress is lumpy and always was – everybody says so, including Jeb – and it has to go – and I guess I'll leave the Lincoln Bathroom alone for now, it has a quaint Fifties air about it and it'll make George happy to keep it the same – he does have his own sense of history, with his project of peeing in all thirty-five of the White House bathrooms and he wants them to be just like they've always been

GEORGE

so I should have said to Pretty Boy from the National Public Radio today that I meant what I said when I said *the tar on wearer* instead of *the war on terror* cause I had on my new boots down in Crawford, see, and the county was resurfacing Mill Road and I got tar on those boots, walking along, so I said what I meant and I meant what I said: I regret the necessity to have tar on the wearer but you got to walk on the road to get someplace in Iraq cause over there they die with their boots on, I should have said that and Pretty Boy would've just scratched his pointy head and I'd've given him my special little knowing smile which I have given to plenty of these pencilheads and they don't even have a clue what that smile means, which is when I'm out of office I'll have each of you that got that smile down to Crawford, one at a time, and you think it's to get a story about the doofus back on his ranch, but when you get there, I'll make you a proposition, each one of you, which is: admit it, you've dreamed about punching me in the nose, you figure I ain't so tough without my Presidential war powers and you figure I'm plenty stupid and you'd like to whip my ass, well now's your chance, just real private, we'll go out to the clearing by Rainey Creek and take off our jackets and we will have it out like real men and I will kick your ass unremittlessly till you're crying for your white-haired little old mama even though she slapped you around pretty good when you were a boy cause that's who you're dealing with. Not the mama. The guy who can whip your ass

117

ROBERT OLEN BUTLER

62, writer, Vietnam veteran

MISS X

36, hotel desk clerk, daughter of North Vietnamese soldier

in room 1503, Sheraton Saigon Hotel and Towers, AUGUST 11, 2007

ROBERT

we washed with Sheraton soap, a Coca-Cola on the night table, CNN muted on the TV screen, the new Saigon outside, fifteen stories below, the motorcycle roar barely audible over the AC fan, she'd reached her hand around her computer and across the registration desk to touch my wrist, an impossibly awkward gesture as if to say *Here is your past in this place, determined to touch you*, and I said *Em đẹp nhu nàng tiên – you are beautiful as a fairy princess*, an old-fashioned compliment she'd never heard from any man, much less an American – and then later she was at my door and we touched lips and we held each other and she whispered softly *Trời oi*, a summoning of God, but familiarly, as if God were a lover passing unaware on the other side of the street, and now as we hold even closer to each other there is a sudden quieting in me: trời oi, since I was first in this city, thirty-six years, four wives, a father, a hundred thousand special moments of the body, my Saigon have all passed: let me kiss her again now, for I am distracted, and I do, and a woman's lips move against mine speaking their own secret language, which, after all the years of my life, I still yearn to understand

MISS X

all I have of him are some photos the size of my palm, my father, he smiles into the sunlight that half closes his eyes, he smiles for the daughter he will never see, and I have a flag, red with a yellow star, carefully folded, and I have stories of his bravery for his country, and there is a certain kind of ghost who comes with irony, who comes in an unexpected form to whisper that it is all right to laugh and to be in a body for a while, and this man I hold now called me something a man would call his daughter and I believe his smile and his hands and I am not yet a ghost so I touched him to begin and I touch him some more and he speaks in a father's voice and I will hold him even closer though once he could have pulled the trigger himself

KEVIN SMITH
38, advertising executive

JULIA HANSON
36, art gallery manager

in her Manhattan apartment, OCTOBER 16, 2007

KEVIN

our words – only an hour ago, in a coffee shop in the West Village, each of us alone at a table, and then an accidental synchronicity of glances over the *Times* and then her hesitation – for it was her decision to make – and then her yes, I'll rise and come to you – our words still run through my head like reefer smoke, smoothing things over, blurring what our bodies remembered of the last time *You look good* I said *So do you* she said *Are you still* she began and I interrupted *No* I said too sharply and I knew she wanted more and I said *Another man* and she laughed, but gently, *Perhaps it was with the man who just left me* she said and we looked into each other's eyes and we knew we were both burned down, we were both rubble, and I move now inside her and she splays her hands hard on my back and when we are done, when I can find my breath, my voice, I will say I'm sorry

JULIA

a thing that was gone all this time, a small thing, now that it has returned I understand how badly I missed it, the thumb edge of his right hand, how as he begins to move inside me he always strokes my hair with that edge of his hand, for a long while, and I turn my face a little in that direction I want to kiss his hand and I imagine these past few years unwinding – I unweep, I unpretend I am in love, I undeceive myself, I unfuck, I unmeet a man I force myself to care for, and I go all the way back to us, to my husband and me, we undivorce, we unfall, we unburn, the world we knew unchanges – but this is a small thing, his familiar hand upon my hair, and I know that even on a bright clear morning something terrible can fly in your window, but until then I will kiss his hand and we will try once more

SANTA CLAUS
471, philanthropist

INGEBIRGITTA
826, elf

in a back room of Santa's workshop, North Pole, JANUARY 2008

SANTA

well well well ho ho ho I am a naughty boy no doubt about it, but she understands, my overstuffed Christmas turkey of a Mrs. Claus, with her hair bunned up tight, the color of Stockholm street slush, and I'm happy to put a lump of coal in my own stocking for the sake of this sweet elf's hair unfurled and floating all about us, filling the room, covering us over, the undulant red of the bottom fringe of an auroral curtain *At least she's an older woman* my plump pudding of a Mrs. Claus says, and it's sad really how she can take comfort from that technicality, for this is our two hundred fifty-second January, my elf and I, and she still looks as young as Barbie, and after my wild night of plunging into chimneys and clothes-drier vents and pussy-cat doors and keyholes I must – even if only from the sympathetic magic of it – fly through the dark passage of my elf and give her gifts *You need to unwind* my bloated-to-bursting goose of a Mrs. Claus says *I'll just bake some cookies* and I am dashing and dancing and cometing and vixening but my Christmas wish once again is that I could just do this and stop thinking about my wife

INGEBIRGITTA

he's been in too many human houses: he is so like them now, he is so distracted, he is indeed so like a bowl full of jelly, where has my good Father Christmas gone, before he got this jolly image and before he got his livestock and his fan mail and his four million Google hits – twice as many as the Easter Bunny, he loves to say – but if only you knew, my dear, how often I think I'd prefer the bunny – though you are a kindly one and you are a merry one and you are a droll one, these are trivial things to me, I am an elf, I am of forest duff and I am of tree-bark dew and I am of quaking top-leaves and I am always of this trembling yearning body and I can dance a man to death, but you are managed now and you are spun and, worst of all, you think too much, and all I really want from you, dear Santa, is a Dirty Decadence 12-Speed Rabbit-Wand Double-Dip Flex-O-Pulse Vibrator

FIN

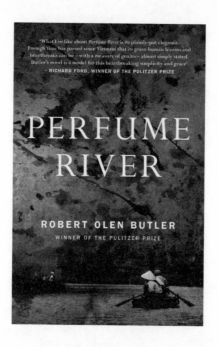

"What I so like about *Perfume River* is its plainly-put elegance. Enough time has passed since Vietnam that its grave human lessons and heartbreaks can be – with a measure of genius – almost simply stated. Butler's novel is a model for this heartbreaking simplicity and grace."
– RICHARD FORD, WINNER OF THE PULITZER PRIZE

PERFUME RIVER

ROBERT OLEN BUTLER
WINNER OF THE PULITZER PRIZE

LONGLISTED FOR THE ANDREW CARNEGIE MEDALS FOR EXCELLENCE 2017

Profound and poignant, *Perfume River* is a masterful novel that examines family ties and the legacy of the Vietnam War through the portrait of a single North Florida family.

Robert Quinlan and his wife Darla teach at Florida State University. Their marriage, forged in the fervor of anti-Vietnam-war protests, now bears the fractures of time, with the couple trapped in an existence of morning coffee and solitary jogging and separate offices. For Robert and Darla, the cracks remain below the surface, whereas the divisions in Robert's own family are more apparent: he has almost no relationship with his brother Jimmy, who became estranged from the family as the Vietnam War intensified. William Quinlan, Robert and Jimmy's father, a veteran of World War II, is coming to the end of his life, and aftershocks of war ripple across all their lives once again when Jimmy refuses to appear at his father's bedside. And a disturbed homeless man whom Robert at first takes to be a fellow Vietnam veteran turns out to have a devastating impact not just on Robert, but on his entire family.

Profound and poignant, *Perfume River* is an examination of relationships, personal choice, and how war resonates down the generations. It is the finest novel yet from the Pulitzer Prize–winning author of *A Good Scent from a Strange Mountain*.

Robert Olen Butler's lyrical and poignant collection of stories about the aftermath of the Vietnam War and its impact on the Vietnamese was acclaimed by critics across the nation and won the Pulitzer Prize in 1993. A contemporary classic by one of America's most important living writers, this edition of *A Good Scent from a Strange Mountain* includes two subsequently published stories that brilliantly complete the collection's narrative journey, returning to the jungles of Vietnam.

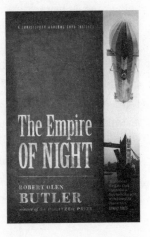

The Hot Country

War correspondent Christopher Marlowe 'Kit' Cobb arrives in Vera Cruz, Mexico, to cover the country's civil war. A passionate believer in the power of a free press and the moral superiority of the United States, Kit is no mere observer. He assumes a false identity to pursue German diplomat Friedrich von Mensinger en route to a meeting with revolutionary leader Pancho Villa, and the correspondent soon finds himself up to his neck in political intrigue. Along the way he's nearly shot by a mysterious sniper, joins forces with a double agent and falls in love with a headstrong young Mexican woman who may be mixed up in the revolutionary plot.

The Star of Istanbul

It is 1915 and Germany has allied itself with the Ottoman empire, persuading the caliphs of Turkey to declare a jihad on the British empire, as President Woodrow Wilson hesitates to enter the fray. War correspondent Christopher Marlowe Cobb has been tasked to follow Brauer, a German intellectual and possible secret service agent suspected of holding information vital to the war effort.

As they travel on the Lusitania's fateful voyage, Cobb becomes smitten with famed actress Selene Bourgani. Cobb soon realizes that this simple actress is anything but, as she harbours secrets that could add fuel to the already raging conflict. Surviving the night of the infamous German U-Boat attack, Cobb follows Selene and Brauer into the darkest alleyways of London and on to the powder keg that is Istanbul. He must use all the cunning he possesses to uncover Selene's true motives, only to realize her hidden agenda could bring down some of the world's most powerful leaders.

The Empire of Night

"Kit" Cobb is working undercover in a castle on the Kent coast owned by a suspected British government mole, Sir Albert Stockman. Kit is working with his mother, the beautiful and mercurial spy, Isabel Cobb, who also happens to be a world-famous stage actress. Isabel's offstage role is to keep tabs on Stockman, while Kit tries to figure out his agenda. Following his mother and her escort from the relative safety of Britain into the lion's den of Berlin, Kit must remain in character, even under the very nose of the Kaiser.

FIN